THE
AMAZING
COLLECTION™

THE
MAJOR
PROPHETS

ISAIAH, JEREMIAH, LAMENTATIONS,

EZEKIEL, AND DANIEL

SET 5

BIG
DREAM
MINISTRIES

No part of *The Amazing Collection*™, whether audio, video, or print, may be reproduced in any form without written permission from Big Dream Ministries, Inc., P.O. Box 324, 12460 Crabapple Road, Suite 202, Alpharetta, Georgia 30004.

ISBN 1-932199-05-5

Cover design by Brand Navigation and Arvid Wallen
Cover composite image by Getty Images and Corbis
Creative Team: Leigh McLeroy, Kathy Mosier, Pat Reinheimer, Glynese Northam

Some of the anecdotal illustrations in this book are true to life and are included with the permission of the persons involved. All other illustrations are composites of real situations, and any resemblance to people living or dead is coincidental.

All Scripture quotations in this publication are taken from the *New American Standard Bible* (NASB), © The Lockman Foundation 1960, 1962, 1963, 1968, 1971, 1972, 1973, 1975, 1977, 1995.

Printed in Canada

2 3 4 5 6 7 8 9 10 / 09 08 07

Welcome to
The Amazing Collection
The Bible, Book by Book

It is amazing how a love letter arriving at just the right time can gladden the heart, refresh the soul, and restore the passion of the beloved. When lovers are separated by distance and can communicate only through the written word, that word becomes the lifeline of their love.

The greatest love letter ever written often sits on our shelves unopened as we go about our lives, sometimes fearful, burdened, anxious, in pain, and in doubt, not knowing that on its pages we can find all we need to live the life we have always wanted.

In this love letter we will discover God, and through Him we will receive hope, assurance, freedom from fear, guidance for everyday life, wisdom, joy, peace, power, and above all, the way to salvation. We will find the life we have always longed for — *abundant* life.

The Bible is simply a love letter compiled into sixty-six books and written over a period of sixteen hundred years by more than forty authors living on three continents. Although the authors came from different backgrounds, there is one message, one theme, one thread that runs throughout the entire Bible from the first book, Genesis, to the last book, Revelation. That message is God's redeeming love for mankind — a message that is as relevant for us today as it was two thousand years ago.

God has written the Bible so that men and women might enter into an intimate relationship with Him and see His character, His works, His power, and His love. It would be tragic to read these books and never come to know your God! Therefore, as you go through this study, listen to the lectures, read the Scripture, and do your daily homework. Make it your heart's desire to know God intimately. Read each page of the Bible as if it were a love letter written by the hand of God to you personally. Bask in His great love, stand in awe of His mighty power, bow before His majesty, and give thanksgiving and adoration to the One who is all-present, all-knowing, all-merciful, and all-loving. He is on every page, and He is speaking to you.

The Bible is a book inspired by God Himself. It is His story, His love letter, His invitation to you to become His child through His Son, Jesus Christ. It is the Word of God . . . indeed, the most Amazing Collection.

CONTENTS

LAMENTATIONS

EZEKIEL

DANIEL

MAPS, CHARTS, AND DIAGRAMS

WORKBOOK GUIDE

The Amazing Collection is a study of the Bible, book by book. This fifth study covers the five major prophetical books of the Bible. The following will acquaint you with the design of this series.

The entire Bible will be studied one book at a time through a teaching video and a written study. The teaching video includes music to stir the heart, graphics to enlighten the mind, and a personal testimony to bring the theme of that particular book to life.

The workbook contains:

1. An introduction to summarize each book.

2. Outlines to be used while watching each of the teaching videos. The answers to the outline blanks are given during the videos and can also be found in the key at the back of your workbook.

3. *Learning for Life* discussion questions to be used after viewing the videos. (If your group is large, we recommend forming small discussion groups.)

4. Five daily lessons of homework for each book.

5. A memory verse for each book.

6. Various maps, charts, and diagrams.

7. A review at the end of each book to refresh your memory. The answers to the review are found in the *Review It!* sections in the margins at the end of the lessons for Day One through Day Four. The fifth review question is a review of the memory verse.

Before you begin the homework, ask God to show you how to apply the truths of Scripture to your own life. At the beginning of each day's lesson in the workbook, there are two choices for the daily reading. The *Complete Read* enables you to read the entire book over the course of that study. During busy times, the *Quick Read* allows you to read a few key chapters or verses from that book. The daily lesson will require a small amount of time each day to complete. Of course, feel free to extend that time with additional study.

One of the incredible things about the Word of God is that you can read the same Scripture at different times in your life and gain new insights with each reading. God's Word is inexhaustible, and it is living; it has the power to produce life-changing results. Our prayer for you as you journey through *The Amazing Collection* is that you will learn for life the purpose, main characters, geography, and time period of every book in the Bible. But above all, we pray that you will come to know more intimately the God of the Bible, His Son Jesus Christ, and the Holy Spirit..

THE MAJOR PROPHETS AT A GLANCE

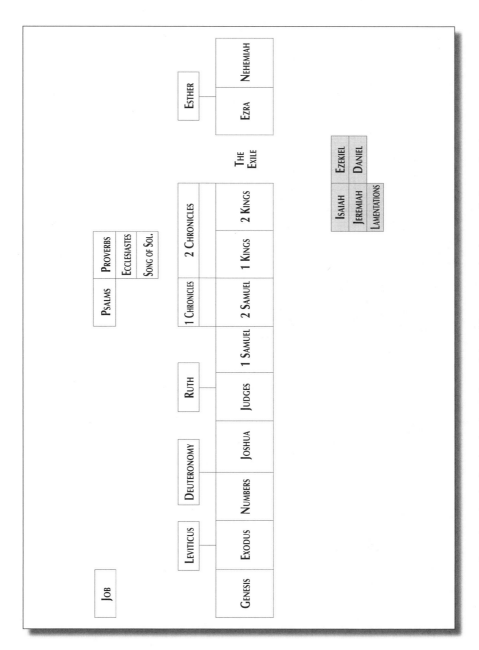

To see how these books fit into the chronology of the Old Testament books as a whole, see the chart on page 146.

KEEPING THE PROPHETS IN PERSPECTIVE

	ISRAEL	JUDAH	EXILE IN BABYLONIA	POST-EXILE JERUSALEM	ASSYRIA	EDOM
800 BC		JOEL 835 BC				OBADIAH 848 BC
700 BC	AMOS 760 BC HOSEA 755 BC	ISAIAH 740 BC MICAH 735 BC			JONAH 793 BC	
722 BC	ISRAEL IS CONQUERED BY ASSYRIA					
600 BC		JEREMIAH 627 BC ZEPHANIAH 632 BC HABAKKUK 609 BC	EZEKIEL 592 BC DANIEL 605 BC		NAHUM 664 BC	
586 BC	JUDAH IS EXILED TO BABYLON					
500 BC			LAMENTATIONS 586 BC	HAGGAI 520 BC ZECHARIAH 520 BC		
400 BC				MALACHI 432 BC		
400 BC ↓ 0 BC	400 SILENT YEARS					

JESUS CHRIST THE MESSIAH IS BORN

The dates listed in this chart are the beginning dates of the prophets' ministry.

OVERVIEW OF THE MAJOR PROPHETS

The following pages provide an overview of each of the books you will be studying in this set. They are designed to be cut out and used as quick reference cards with the main facts of the book on the front and the memory verse on the back.

You might find it helpful to laminate them and carry them with you on a ring or keep them in a card holder in a place where you'll be able to refer to them often.

It is our hope that this will be a tool that will help you truly learn these books for life.

ISAIAH
Israel's Messiah Promised

WHO:

Isaiah

Nation of Judah

WHAT:

Prophecy of God's Judgment and Future Salvation

WHERE:

Jerusalem

Time Covered: 60 Years

JEREMIAH
Jerusalem's Final Judgment

WHO:

Jeremiah

WHAT:

Jerusalem's Final Forty Years and Her Destruction

WHERE:

Judah

Time Covered: 47 Years

LAMENTATIONS
Jerusalem's Destruction Mourned

WHO:

Jeremiah

People of Jerusalem

WHAT:

Jeremiah Mourned Jerusalem's Destruction

WHERE:

Jerusalem

Time Written: 586 BC

ISAIAH
Israel's Messiah Promised

"Come now, and let us reason together,"
Says the Lord,
"Though your sins are as scarlet,
They will be as white as snow;
Though they are red like crimson,
They will be like wool."

ISAIAH 1:18

JEREMIAH
Jerusalem's Final Judgment

"For My people have forgotten Me,
They burn incense to worthless gods
And they have stumbled from their ways,
From the ancient paths,
To walk in bypaths,
Not on a highway."

JEREMIAH 18:15

LAMENTATIONS
Jerusalem's Destruction Mourned

The LORD's lovingkindnesses indeed never cease,
For His compassions never fail.
They are new every morning;
Great is Your faithfulness.

LAMENTATIONS 3:22-23

EZEKIEL
Israel's Eventual Restoration

WHO:

Ezekiel

WHAT:

God's Glory
Would Depart but
Eventually Return

WHERE:

Tel-Abib in
Babylonia

Time Covered: 22 Years

DANIEL
God's Supremacy over Nations

WHO:

Daniel

Meshach

Shadrach

Abednego

King
Nebuchadnezzar

WHAT:

Exiles Encouraged by
Daniel's Experiences
and Prophecies

WHERE:

Babylonia

Time Covered: 69 Years

EZEKIEL
Israel's Eventual Restoration

Then the Spirit lifted me up, and I heard a great rumbling sound behind me, "Blessed be the glory of the LORD in His place."

EZEKIEL 3:12

DANIEL
God's Supremacy over Nations

*Let the name of God be blessed forever and ever,
For wisdom and power belong to Him.*

DANIEL 2:20

INTRODUCTION TO THE MAJOR PROPHETS

We are beginning a study of an entirely different kind of literature. The first seventeen books of the Bible (Genesis–Esther) are historical, filled with fast-moving narrative. The next five books (Job–Song of Solomon) are poetical, overflowing with deep emotion. And now the last seventeen books of the Old Testament (Isaiah–Malachi) are prophetical, serving up predictions about the future and preaching that has no equal.

These last seventeen books can be categorized as The Major Prophets (Isaiah–Daniel) and The Minor Prophets (Hosea–Malachi). The terms *major* and *minor* have nothing to do with the prominence of the authors or the importance of the material. The terms were first used because of the greater length of most of the first five books compared to the last twelve.

The five books of The Major Prophets cover a significant time span and present a wide array of messages. Isaiah spoke to the nation of Judah about 150 years before their exile into Babylonia and called them to be faithful to God. Jeremiah cried out to those same people on the brink of that exile and pleaded for their repentance. Lamentations, written by Jeremiah, presents a dirge as Judah went into exile. The last two major prophets, Ezekiel and Daniel, spoke and wrote to the people in exile, encouraging them to remember that God was still in control and would eventually restore the spiritual fortunes of His disciplined nation.

Three of these five books are quite long, and all of them can, at times, be difficult to understand. However, the time and effort invested in striving to understand these writings will pay huge dividends. It has been said that no other section of the Bible offers such a majestic and highly exalted picture of God. His sovereignty is mind-boggling. His glory is breathtaking. And in reading these books, our faith finds new depths of confidence.

Get ready now to meet once again the God of the prophecies and to be amazed at the prophecies of God as they unfold in these first five prophetical books.

ISAIAH

ONE

[Israel's Messiah Promised]

"Come now, and let us reason together,"

Says the LORD,

"Though your sins are as scarlet,

They will be as white as snow;

Though they are red like crimson,

They will be like wool."

ISAIAH 1:18

ISAIAH
[Israel's Messiah Promised]

INTRODUCTION

During Israel's and Judah's years of apostasy and rebellion, God raised up prophets to warn His people of coming judgment. These prophets both *foretold* (told before it happened) and *told forth* (spoke in place of another). Isaiah was the first of the major prophets who spoke for God. This book is sometimes called "The Gospel of Isaiah" because of his clear prophecies of God's coming wrath and a coming Savior.

Isaiah's place as the first of the Bible's prophetical books could not be more appropriate. As a man, Isaiah was influential as a political adviser to kings, brilliant as a predictor of future events, passionate as a preacher of moral truth, and unsurpassed as a model for godliness.

Isaiah's call by God to ministry teaches us much about God as He truly is, and his response to that call teaches us much about people as they should be. Isaiah's humility, sensitivity, and availability are worth much reflection on our part.

But as much as we should admire and seek to emulate Isaiah, our true focus in this book should be on God. In many ways, God is never held up "bigger" before the eyes of our heart than in Isaiah. Isaiah 53 stands out as one of the most famous chapters in the Bible. This picture of the Messiah as God's suffering Servant is both precise in its details and heartrending in its passion. Over and over, this book implies and states directly that there is no one like God and no other God besides Him.

Get ready to encounter our big God and be brought to new levels of heart worship as you meditate on the truths of Isaiah this week.

Isaiah
[Israel's Messiah Promised]

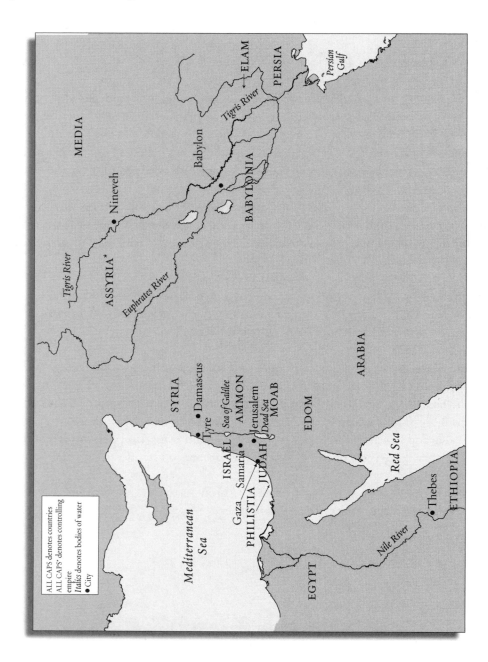

ALL CAPS denotes countries
ALL CAPS* denotes controlling empire
Italics denotes bodies of water
• City

I SAIAH
[Israel's Messiah Promised]

OVERVIEW

WHO: Author: Isaiah
Main Characters: Isaiah and the nation of Judah

WHAT: Prophecy warning of God's judgment for rebellion; prophecy promising hope through God's salvation

WHEN: Isaiah's ministry of sixty years during the time of 2 Kings (740–680 BC)

WHERE: Jerusalem

WHY: To call Judah to repentance and hope in the coming Messiah

I. ISAIAH'S PROPHECY OF JUDGMENT—NEED FOR SALVATION
   (ISAIAH 1–35)

   A. _____ had rebelled and would be judged by being exiled.

   B. Isaiah saw God as _____ and _____—high, lifted up, exalted, and holy.

   C. When Isaiah was in God's presence he:

      1. Was _____ of his sin.

      2. _____ his sin.

      3. Was _____ of his sin.

      4. Was _____ to go for the Lord.

   D. _____ had rebelled and would be judged by Assyria.

   E. Ten _____ had rebelled and would be judged.

   F. The entire _____ had rebelled and would be judged "in that day."

II. HISTORICAL TRANSITION—FROM ASSYRIA TO BABYLON (ISAIAH 36–39)

A. The _____ were threatening to invade Judah.

B. Hezekiah became mortally _____.

C. Hezekiah was proud. He showed the king of _____
all the riches of Judah.

III. ISAIAH'S PROPHECY OF HOPE—PROVISION OF SALVATION
(ISAIAH 40–66)

A. Isaiah prophesied a _____ calling, "clear the way for the Lord."

B. Isaiah prophesied _____ would rebuild Jerusalem and the
temple.

C. Isaiah prophesied a _____ would come. The Savior would:

1. _____ His people.

2. _____ for sinners.

3. _____ everybody to come to Him.

4. Heal the brokenhearted and _____ the prisoner.

D. Isaiah prophesied the Savior also would (at His second coming):

1. _____ with vengeance.

2. _____ Israel.

3. _____ a new heaven and a new earth.

4. _____ as King of kings.

APPLICATION

Reading Isaiah is like reading a gospel—there is a clear picture of both our
sin and our Savior. How awesome that seven hundred years before Jesus
was born, God revealed the One who was coming to comfort us, suffer for
us, and free us! And He is not done. He has promised to come again to
judge, restore, and reign. Can you, like Isaiah, see Him high and lifted up?
Then bow down before your King and say, "Here am I. Send me!"

ISAIAH
[Israel's Messiah Promised]

LEARNING FOR LIFE

1. What did you learn about prophets? Why did God send them?

2. What was happening in the world and in Isaiah's life that caused God to send him as a prophet at that particular time?

3. Review some of the prophecies Isaiah made that have come true.

4. Review some of the prophecies Isaiah made that have not yet come true.

5. Isaiah foretold the coming of Christ and described two chief roles for Him. What were those roles? (See Hebrews 9:28.)

6. What from Isaiah's life experiences could you apply to your own life?

ISAIAH
[Israel's Messiah Promised]

DAY ONE

COMPLETE READ: Chapters 1–14
QUICK READ: Chapters 7–9

THE BIG PICTURE

Every now and then a man or woman comes along who simply dominates their era. Isaiah was such a person. During the years he ministered as a prophet in and to the nation of Judah, he was without equal. He was a statesman of the finest order, giving Kings Ahaz and Hezekiah much-needed, but often rejected, counsel. (Hindsight invariably proved Isaiah was right.) But he was also the prophet of all prophets. His message was far-reaching and awesome. His God was a big God. And from this God he received messages for his people that were nothing less than life- and world-changing.

J. Sidlow Baxter in *Explore the Book* writes,

> What Beethoven is in the realm of music, what Shakespeare is in the realm of literature, what Spurgeon was among the Victorian preachers, that is Isaiah among the prophets. As a writer he transcends all his prophet compeers; and it is fitting that the matchless contribution from his pen should stand as leader to the seventeen prophetical books.[1]

Greatness after all, in spite of its name, appears to be not so much a certain size as a certain quality in human lives. It may be present in lives whose range is very small.

—PHILLIPS BROOKS, nineteenth-century Episcopal bishop

Isaiah's long ministry spanned sixty years, from 740 to 680 BC, and touched the reign of four kings: Uzziah, Jotham, Ahaz, and Hezekiah. While ministering to the southern kingdom of Judah, he watched the northern kingdom of Israel be taken captive by Assyria. He saw Judah following the same idolatrous path as their northern brethren and warned them of the judgment to come if they failed to heed God's call for repentance:

> "Come now, and let us reason together,"
> Says the LORD,
> "Though your sins are as scarlet,
> They will be as white as snow;
> Though they are red like crimson,
> They will be like wool." (Isaiah 1:18)

Isaiah warned Judah that Babylonia, not Assyria, would be used as God's disciplinary rod against them, even though Babylonia had not yet risen to world power.

In contrast to the judgment of the first part of his book, the second half is filled with the hope of God's sovereignty and salvation.

Isaiah and the complete Bible share an interesting symmetry. The Bible has sixty-six books. Isaiah has sixty-six chapters. The Bible has two Testaments, the Old with thirty-nine books and the New with twenty-seven. Isaiah has two general divisions, the first with thirty-nine chapters (including the historical transition in chapters 36–39) and the second with twenty-seven.

The chart that follows can help you visualize the content and structure of the book of Isaiah.

JUDGMENT	**TRANSITION**	**HOPE**
1. On Judah 2. On the Nations 3. On the Earth	1. Assyria 2. Babylonia	1. Sovereignty of God 2. Servant of God 3. Standards of God
1 35	36 39	40 66
Prophecy	History	Prophecy

Salvation is so simple we can overlook it, so profound we can never comprehend it.
—UNKNOWN

The theme of Isaiah is that salvation is of God. This shines through in many different ways:

- The word *salvation* occurs twenty-six times in Isaiah but only seven times in all the other prophets combined.

- The name *Isaiah* means "Jehovah is Salvation."

- Chapter 53 presents the suffering Servant who will come to provide salvation.

- Chapters 1–39 graphically display the *need* for salvation.

- Chapters 40–66 picture the full *provision* of salvation.

The historical transition section (chapters 36–39) records the interaction between King Hezekiah of Judah and Isaiah the prophet. Chapters 36–37 deal with Hezekiah's relationship with Assyria, and chapters 38–39 deal with his relationship with Babylonia. It seems Isaiah virtually had an open door to Hezekiah's throne room.

In *A History of Israel*, John Bright states,

> In all her history, Israel produced few figures of greater stature than Isaiah. . . . For fifty years he towered over the contemporary scene and though perhaps few in his day realized it, more than any other individual, guided the nation through her hour of tragedy and crisis.[2]

As you read Isaiah this week, ask God to help you see two things:

1. The greatness of this man Isaiah—a veiled but visible greatness behind the beautiful curtain of humility

2. The greatness of the God Isaiah portrayed in all majesty through his message

MEMORY VERSE

"Come now, and let us reason together,"
Says the LORD,
"Though your sins are as scarlet,
They will be as white as snow;
Though they are red like crimson,
They will be like wool."

ISAIAH 1:18

ISAIAH
[Israel's Messiah Promised]

DAY TWO

COMPLETE READ: Chapters 15–27
QUICK READ: Chapter 1

THINK ABOUT IT
Isaiah has been called
the "Saint Paul of the
Old Testament."

A CRUCIAL CHAPTER

Stand them on end just close enough to each other so that when one falls, it will knock over the next, which will knock over the next, and the next, and the next. It's an amusing way to play with dominoes. And it also illustrates how one aspect of life often affects another. It's called the domino effect.

Isaiah 1, our Crucial Chapter, illustrates the domino effect. One sin leads to another, which then leads to another. If this historic scene took place in a courtroom, it might look something like this:

- God is the judge.

- The heavens and earth are the jury (Isaiah 1:2).

- Judah is the defendant.

- Isaiah is the prosecuting attorney.

- The crime consists of three counts of sin.

- The options for settlement are judgment or blessing.

The chart on the next page pictures the flow of the chapter.

Each section describes a sin for which God rebuked His people. The call to repentance comes in the middle of the second section. If they refused to repent, their judgment was spelled out in regard to each sin. But even if they chose not to repent, God always promised hope following judgment. These four themes

All human sin seems so much worse in its consequences than in its intentions.

—REINHOLD NIEBUHR,
German theologian,
preacher, and activist

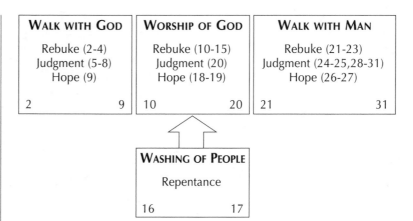

are a helpful way to look at not only Isaiah 1 or the entire book of Isaiah, but all the prophetical books. Almost every verse fits one of the four categories:

1. God *rebuked* the people.

2. God called for *repentance*.

3. If they refused, God brought *judgment*.

4. Following judgment, *hope* was always offered.

Using these four categories as your guide, describe each of the three sins for which God rebuked the people. In addition, read through the verses on judgment and hope to get a feel for the fourfold pattern. Refer to the previous chart for the Scripture references on judgment and hope.

1:2-4

1:10-15

Of our own we have nothing but sin.

—Saint Augustine of Hippo, Carthaginian author, saint, and church father

Here is one way to summarize these three sins and their relationship to each other:

SIN NUMBER 1 (1:2-4):	Turning from God	"They have abandoned the LORD." (verse 4)
SIN NUMBER 2 (1:10-15):	Turning to ritual	"I cannot endure iniquity and the solemn assembly." (verse 13)
SIN NUMBER 3 (1:21-23):	Turning from justice	"She who was full of justice!" (verse 21)

Israel abandoned their walk with God. Then, they turned their worship of God into ritual. Finally, they filled their walk with each other with injustice. The domino effect! One thing led to the other. And it all began with abandoning their personal, intimate relationship with God as their Father (1:2) and their Master (1:3).

Do you see yourself anywhere in this picture? Is there a sin God is rebuking you for that you are ignoring?

Are you experiencing, or are you about to experience, the discipline of God because of that sin?

One of the most fundamental marks of true repentance is a disposition to see our sins as God sees them.

—CHARLES SIMEON, British teacher and promoter of missionary work

If you are, you can be sure there is hope that God can bring good from anything. But repentance—not mere regret or remorse—must come from your heart. Remember, the righteous Judge is on your side. He wants to give you a settlement of blessing.

REVIEW IT!
Chapter 1 is our Crucial Chapter because it pictures the fourfold theme of the prophets and shows the domino effect of sin.

MEMORY VERSE

"Come now, and let us reason together,"
Says the LORD,
"Though your sins are as scarlet,
They will be as white as snow;
Though they are red like crimson,
They will be like wool."

ISAIAH 1:18

ISAIAH
[Israel's Messiah Promised]

DAY THREE

COMPLETE READ: Chapters 28–39
QUICK READ: Chapters 5–6

REMEMBER
Isaiah was a
contemporary of
Hosea, a prophet to
Israel, and Micah, a
prophet to Judah.

A PROMINENT PLAYER

Os Guinness, in his book *The Call*, writes of Leonardo da Vinci that even though he was handsome, strong, and very gifted, he began life with great modesty. At a young age, he copied into his notebook:

> *Let him who cannot do the thing he would*
> *Will to do what he can. To will is foolish*
> *Where there's no power to do. That man is wise*
> *Who, if he cannot, does not wish he could.*

But da Vinci soon left such cautious modesty behind. Throughout his adult life, whether in Florence, Milan, Rome, or France, he was bent on stretching the limits of his powers. Others, both then and later, said that da Vinci would have been wiser to concentrate on a few gifts rather than the many that comprised his genius. This lack of focus, they said, was why he "procrastinated" while others, like Michelangelo, "produced." Vasari himself regretted that da Vinci had not kept to painting rather than pursuing his myriad inventions that were years, sometimes centuries, before their time. . . . Only months before da Vinci died in 1519, he returned to the church of Santa Maria delle Grazie in Milan to discover that damp was already breaking through his fresco of the *Last Supper*. The maestro's greatest masterpieces were unfinished, destroyed, or

The responsible person seeks to make his or her whole life a response to the question and call of God.

—DIETRICH BONHOEFFER, German Protestant theologian and anti-Nazi activist decaying in his own lifetime. One day, not long before he died at the royal palace of Cloux in the Loire Valley, he wrote in his notebook in unusually small script (as if, one writer commented, he were a little ashamed): "We should not desire the impossible."[3]

It's interesting to speculate but impossible to know what God's call for da Vinci actually was and whether or not he followed it. But one thing we can be sure of is the truth of Danish philosopher Søren Kierkegaard's advice, written in his *Journal*, as it applies to da Vinci and to us:

> The thing is to understand myself, to see what God really wants me to do; the thing is to find a truth which is true for me, to find the idea for which I can live and die.[4]

Our Prominent Player, the prophet Isaiah, knew with clarity what God wanted him to do. In chapter 6 he found the thing for which, in Kierkegaard's words, he could "live and die." In this chapter God called Isaiah to his life's work. And what a scene it was!

Read Isaiah 6:1-4, which is the setting for Isaiah's call. Use your own words or phrases to describe what this incredible scene must have been like.

Isaiah's response is in verse 5. Write a paraphrase of this verse to describe the depth of emotion and humility that Isaiah must have felt.

Read verses 6 and 7. What do you imagine Isaiah was thinking and feeling at this time? If you have artistic ability, try to capture this scene in some creative way.

The awareness of the holiness of God (verses 1-4) led to Isaiah's sense of utter sinfulness (verse 5). After God responded to this humility with cleansing (verses 6-7), Isaiah was prepared to receive and accept God's special call on his life (verses 8-13).

The call was couched in language difficult to understand, but it included delivering to the people a hard message about their sin. Describe it in your own words as best you can.

Blessed is he who has found his work; let him ask no other blessedness.

—THOMAS CARLYLE, nineteenth-century essayist and historian

Obviously, we don't all receive our calling from God in a way as dramatic, compelling, or awe-inspiring as Isaiah's. His was unique. But the Scriptures are clear that God has planned for each of us special assignments to carry out for His glory. None of us is here to simply live out our appointed years and then call it quits.

Often the process of clarifying our individual call from God takes time—sometimes many years. Where are you in that process? What question do you have for God about it at this point in your life? Take time right now to pursue this with Him.

MEMORY VERSE

"Come now, and let us reason together,"
Says the LORD,
"Though your sins are as scarlet,
They will be as white as snow;
Though they are red like crimson,
They will be like wool."

ISAIAH 1:18

ISAIAH
[Israel's Messiah Promised]

NOTE
Isaiah 53 is quoted
or alluded to eighty-
five times in the New
Testament.

DAY FOUR

COMPLETE READ: Chapters 40–53
QUICK READ: Chapters 52–53

A NOTABLE FEATURE

O sacred head, now wounded, with grief and shame weighed
    down,
Now scornfully surrounded with thorns, Thy only crown,
How art Thou pale with anguish, with sore abuse and scorn!
How does that visage languish which once was bright as morn!

What Thou, my Lord, hast suffered was all for sinners' gain;
Mine, mine was the transgression, but Thine the deadly pain.
Lo, here I fall, my Savior! 'Tis I deserve Thy place;
Look on me with Thy favor, vouch-safe to me Thy grace.[5]

"Rhythmica Oration," a seven-part medieval poem, speaks of the
different wounds Christ suffered on the cross—wounds to His
feet, knees, hands, side, breast, heart, and face.[6] This hymn, "O
Sacred Head, Now Wounded," comes from the last portion of
the poem.

*The cross is God's
centerpiece on the
table of time.*
—PAUL GUTTKE,
author on missions and
postmodernism

No hymn is better suited to introduce our Notable Feature:
Isaiah 53, the "Calvary of the Old Testament." Midway between
chapters 40–66, the hope or salvation segment of this book,
God locates the central figure and event of that hope: the person
and suffering of His Son, Jesus Christ our Savior. Written over
seven hundred years before Christ suffered on the cross, every
detail of its description came true on that darkest day of history
outside the gate of the city of Jerusalem.

Reflect and meditate your way through this great, solemn chapter. As you do, respond to the following questions.

List the specific predictions of Isaiah 53 that you know have been fulfilled.

Verse 7 says, "Like a lamb that is led to slaughter." As you consider the place of the lamb in the Old Testament sacrificial system, what thoughts does this passage conjure up about Jesus as the Lamb?

Don't miss the concept of substitution here: Jesus in place of you, Jesus instead of you. Write down the phrases indicating substitution in verses 4-6,8,11-12. As you do this, replace the pronouns (our, we, us, and so on) with your name.

*We never move on
from the cross of
Christ, only into a more
profound understanding
of the cross.*

—DAVID PRIOR, author
and New Testament
scholar

What welled up in your heart as you inserted your name into these phrases, identifying yourself as the cause of Jesus' sufferings?

As you thank God for His mighty gift of grace and salvation, you might conclude your prayer with these words from the third verse of "O Sacred Head, Now Wounded":

> *What language shall I borrow to thank Thee, dearest friend,*
> *For this Thy dying sorrow, Thy pity without end?*
> *O make me Thine forever; and, should I fainting be,*
> *Lord, let me never, never outlive my love for Thee!* [7]

MEMORY VERSE

"Come now, and let us reason together,"
Says the LORD,
"Though your sins are as scarlet,
They will be as white as snow;
Though they are red like crimson,
They will be like wool."

ISAIAH 1:18

REVIEW IT!
Chapter 53 is our
Notable Feature
because of its
prediction of the
suffering of Jesus for
our salvation.

I SAIAH
[Israel's Messiah Promised]

DAY FIVE

COMPLETE READ: Chapters 54–66
QUICK READ: Chapter 40

A TIMELESS PRINCIPLE

The greatest single distinguishing feature of the omnipotence of God is that our imagination gets lost thinking about it.

—BLAISE PASCAL, seventeenth-century French mathematician, physicist, and theologian

God is very kind and good and handsome too. God has given me and some people what we want. He is good. I think He has a white coat and black hair.

God is the Father of Jesus. I like God because He puts ideas into my head when I am in trouble with my sums. Jesus is kind because He helps people who are sick.

I think that God is a very nice man and is very kind to everyone. Even when you or I do something wrong God will forgive us. He punishes people when they do something very bad. He invented schools.

I think God is like us. He is very kind to animals.

—A GROUP OF NINE-YEAR-OLDS WRITING ABOUT GOD

If asked to describe God, adults might be a bit more sophisticated than these children, but it is true that, left to our own devices, we tend to minimize God. As an old saying goes, "God created man in His own image, and man has been returning the compliment ever since."

Even God recognizes this tendency in us. In Psalm 50:21 He says,

These things you have done and I kept silence;
You thought that I was just like you;
I will reprove you and state the case in order before your
     eyes.

It is good for us to examine passages of Scripture that show that God is not like us—not even close! Isaiah 40 is one of those passages, and it surfaces as our Timeless Principle.

Judah was downhearted. They had watched the northern kingdom of Israel fall to Assyria, had felt their own godliness wane, and had heard Isaiah's unbridled predictions of judgment because of their sin. Chapter 40 begins,

"Comfort, O comfort My people," says your God.
"Speak kindly to Jerusalem."

God was not promising to remove deserved judgment, but He was promising hope after judgment. And that hope—that blessing—could only be based on who He was and what He could do. Beginning in verse 12, Isaiah demonstrated proof beyond all doubt that God is not like us and that He can take care of all our needs.

Read Isaiah 40:12-20 and in your own words describe how God is pictured.

UNBELIEVABLE!
One flash of lightning produces enough power to keep a house lit for thirty-five years!

The work done by human effort cannot be compared to the divine work done by God in the creature by His goodness for the sake of the creature.

—MARGUERITE PORETE, thirteenth-century mystic and martyr

After showing the impotence of idols as compared to the power of God in verses 18-20, Isaiah added to the already astounding picture of God in verses 21-26. Read this passage and again describe God's greatness in your own words.

Read what Isaiah said in 40:27-31 about the God who made the world and controls its massive power. Then respond to the following questions.

What does this passage say about God?

Essence beyond essence, Nature increate, Framer of the world, I set Thee, Lord, before my face. I lift up my soul to Thee, I worship Thee on my knees, and humble myself under Thy mighty hand.

—LANCELOT ANDREWES, bishop of Chichester

What is God's power able to do for us?

God is not like us—not at all! And because of His greatness He can empower us when we are weak and weary. How is your strength today? Where are you weak? Weary? In what areas do you need to admit your helplessness and wait on God for power, strength, and renewal? Write them down and then acknowledge to Him that only His greatness can empower you in your weakness.

MEMORY VERSE

"Come now, and let us reason together,"
Says the LORD,
"Though your sins are as scarlet,
They will be as white as snow;
Though they are red like crimson,
They will be like wool."

ISAIAH 1:18

I SAIAH
[Israel's Messiah Promised]

REVIEW

1. The theme of Isaiah is that _____ is of God.

2. Chapter 1 is our Crucial Chapter because it pictures the fourfold theme of the prophets and shows the domino effect of _____ .

3. Isaiah is our Prominent Player whose call by God can teach us much about our

   _____ .

4. Chapter 53 is our Notable Feature because of its description of the future _____ of Jesus for our salvation.

5. "'Come now, and let us reason together,'
   Says the LORD,
   'Though your _____ are as scarlet,
   They will be white as snow;
   Though they are red like crimson,
   They will be like wool.'"

   ISAIAH 1:_____

JEREMIAH

[Jerusalem's Final Judgment]

"For My people have forgotten Me,

They burn incense to worthless gods

And they have stumbled from their ways,

From the ancient paths,

To walk in bypaths,

Not on a highway."

JEREMIAH 18:15

JEREMIAH
[Jerusalem's Final Judgment]

INTRODUCTION

From time to time God calls individuals to a ministry in which there is no apparent success—at least not as we would define success. Jeremiah was one of these men, his ministry one of these ministries. Never has faithfulness been better defined and demonstrated than in the life and ministry of this second major prophet.

Called by God to give His people one last warning, one last chance, one last appeal, Jeremiah preached his heart out for forty years. He was ignored, rejected, and laughed at. He was scorned, rebuked, and mocked. But he plodded on—loving his fellow countrymen, depending on his God, and remaining faithful to his calling.

His countrymen were citizens of the nation of Judah, who, following a roller coaster ride of spiritual ups and downs, were now down for what would prove to be the last time.

How grateful we should be for this inspired record of a man living out faithfulness when he most likely did not feel like being faithful. And the best part? The very God who embraced and empowered Jeremiah in his difficulties is the same yesterday, today, and forever—even in your life.

JEREMIAH
[Jerusalem's Final Judgment]

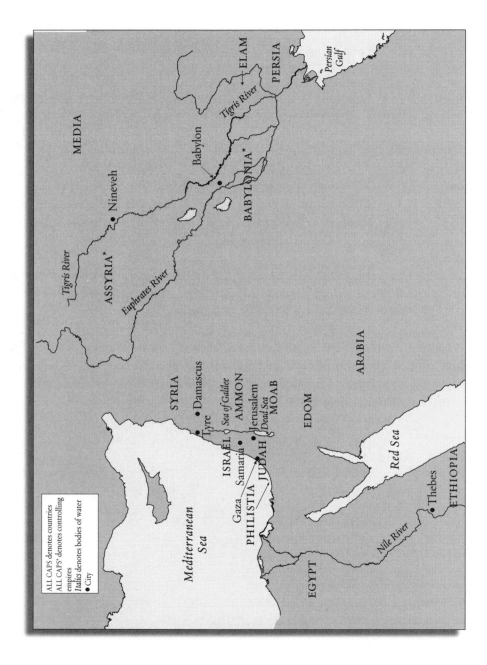

ALL CAPS denotes countries
ALL CAPS' denotes controlling empires
Italics denotes bodies of water
• City

MEDIA

ELAM

PERSIA

Persian Gulf

Tigris River

BABYLONIA*

Babylon

Nineveh

Tigris River

ASSYRIA*

Euphrates River

SYRIA

• Damascus

Tyre

Sea of Galilee

AMMON

Jerusalem

Dead Sea

MOAB

ISRAEL

Samaria

JUDAH

Gaza

PHILISTIA

EDOM

ARABIA

Red Sea

ETHIOPIA

• Thebes

Nile River

EGYPT

Mediterranean Sea

JEREMIAH
[Jerusalem's Final Judgment]

OVERVIEW

WHO: Jeremiah

WHAT: Prophesied to Judah during the final forty years before her destruction

WHEN: 627–580 BC

WHERE: Judah

WHY: Warned of the coming judgment and destruction of Jerusalem

I.   THE TIMES OF JEREMIAH

A. King _____ reigned thirty-one years and brought about a spiritual revival.

    1. He rid Judah of all the _____ .

    2. Josiah _____ in a battle with Egypt.

B. The people chose _____ , Josiah's middle son, to serve as king.

    1. He served for _____ months.

    2. He was exiled to _____ and died there.

C. Egypt put _____ , Josiah's firstborn, on the throne.

    1. He was an _____ king.

    2. He served _____ years.

    3. He taxed the people heavily and forced them to build his _____ .

    4. Jeremiah pronounced a _____ on him.

    5. Jehoikim died of _____ causes.

D. _____ , Jehoikim's son, became king.

    1. He reigned three _____ .

    2. He was exiled to _____ .

E. Babylon put _____ on the throne, and he reigned eleven years.

    1. Babylon laid a _____ around Jerusalem for eighteen months.

2. In July 586 BC, Jerusalem and the _____ were utterly destroyed.

II. THE MAN JEREMIAH

A. God _____ Jeremiah before he was born.

B. Jeremiah was commanded not to _____ , have children, or attend funerals or celebrations.

C. Jeremiah endured incredible _____ .

D. He was a man of incredible _____ and tender emotions.

E. He was spared by Nebuchadnezzar and offered _____ he wanted.

F. He chose to stay in _____ .

G. He wrote a letter to the exiles in _____ and encouraged them to settle down there.

H. He gave hope and encouragement by predicting the exiles would return after _____ years.

III. THE MINISTRY AND MESSAGE OF JEREMIAH

A. Josiah's reign: Jeremiah condemned Judah for false worship and promised _____ .

B. Jehoiakim's reign: Jeremiah promised _____ for the continuous rebellion against God.

C. Zedekiah's reign: He urged Judah to _____ to Babylon and be saved or face God's judgment.

D. Gedaliah's rule: Jeremiah _____ to those left in Jerusalem.

E. Jeremiah predicted the coming _____ and the Millennial Kingdom.

F. He prophesied judgment on _____ nations.

APPLICATION

Jeremiah preached God's Word when none of the people around him wanted to listen. Though abused both verbally and physically, he stayed the course with God, trusting Him even when everyone else was against him. Do you endure with "Jeremiah tenacity" when things get tough?

JEREMIAH
[Jerusalem's Final Judgment]

LEARNING FOR LIFE

1. Review the five kings who reigned during Jeremiah's lifetime.

2. Jeremiah faced great ridicule because he spoke the Word of God and the people did not want to obey. In what ways do we see disobedience to God's Word today?

3. Jeremiah showed great perseverance in trying to warn Judah of the coming judgment.

   a. In what ways was he persecuted?

   b. In what ways did he persevere?

4. God's covenant with Israel promised blessing for obedience, yet Israel consistently disobeyed. Who would mediate a new covenant for God's people? (See Jeremiah 31:31-40; Romans 11:26-27; Hebrews 8:6.)

5. Would you want to be a prophet? Why or why not?

JEREMIAH
[Jerusalem's Final Judgment]

DAY ONE

COMPLETE READ: Chapters 1–11
QUICK READ: Chapters 1 and 52

THE BIG PICTURE

King Josiah of Judah had done well. He had brought serious revival and reformation to the nation of Judah at a time when sin had been easily winning the day. But once a little time passed and the heat of reformation cooled, sin again took center stage in the nation. Into this scene of hopelessness stepped the prophet Jeremiah, the son of Hilkiah. Jeremiah pleaded. He wept. He predicted judgment to come if the people refused to repent. He preached without hesitation, but in the end, the people would not listen.

They did not simply ignore his appeals; they turned on him because of his message of coming judgment. Jeremiah's life reads like a catalog of catastrophe: attempts were made on his life; his relatives abandoned him; a priest had him beaten and put in stocks; many wanted to see him hang as a traitor; the king burned his scroll of prophecies in the fire; leaders incarcerated him; and his enemies threw him into a cistern. For forty years Jeremiah endured this ill treatment without giving up. In the end, the judgment he predicted occurred. Babylonia invaded and defeated Judah in 586 BC and carried the people into exile. Jeremiah had been right, and God's people were wrong to ignore him.

It is difficult to miss the theme of Jeremiah: judgment, judgment, judgment. Of the 1,364 verses in the book, 222 of them deal exclusively with the coming fall of Jerusalem to Babylonia.

The servant of Christ must never be surprised if he has to drink of the same cup with his Lord.
—J. C. RYLE, Anglican minister and defender of the evangelical reformed faith

In addition, another six complete chapters predict judgment against ten other nations. The chart that follows shows the major divisions of the book.

NOTE
Jeremiah is quoted
forty times in the New
Testament.

Call of Jeremiah	Prophecies for the Jews	Prophecies for the Gentiles	Fall of Jerusalem
Mission Announced	Judgment and Hope	Judgment	Mission Accomplished
1	2 45	46 51	52

Jeremiah 1:1 clearly states that Jeremiah authored the book bearing his name. He was the son of a priest of Anathoth, a town about three miles northeast of Jerusalem. He received his call from God to minister in the thirteenth year of the reign of King Josiah, 627 BC (1:2). Jeremiah witnessed the great reformation that took place under King Josiah after the book of the law was found in the temple (review the 2 Kings, Day Five study).

But that reform, great as it was, was too little too late. Following this brief revival, Jeremiah ministered for forty years in an atmosphere of hopeless decline. His prophetic ministry spanned the reigns of the last five kings of Judah. The following chart shows these kings and the portions of Jeremiah relevant to each of them.

Perseverance is not a long race; it is many short races one after another.

—WALTER ELLIOTT

Josiah *31 years*	Jehoahaz *3 months*	Jehoiakim *12 years*	Jehoiachin *3 months*	Zedekiah *11 years*
Chapters 1–6	Chapter 22	Chapters 7–20; 25–26; 35–36; 45–49	Chapters 22–23	Chapters 21; 24; 27–34; 37–39
640 BC 609	609	609 597	597	597 586

627 BC ——————→ JEREMIAH'S MINISTRY ——————→ 580

Your Quick Read for today is chapters 1 and 52, the beginning and end of Jeremiah. Chapter 1 describes Jeremiah's call and mission: to tell the people that judgment was coming from a foreign nation because of their rebellion. Chapter 52 depicts the fall of Jerusalem, proving that Jeremiah's prophecies were true:

God did send His people into exile in Babylonia.

About forty years separate these two chapters. This week, as you read and experience those years through the eyes and pen of Jeremiah, make a concentrated effort to imagine what he might have been thinking, feeling, and experiencing.

Was there a time in your life when you felt you had to persevere against all odds? If you can, briefly describe it.

How did that difficult time in your life affect your relationship with God?

As you finish today, read chapter 1 again and ask God to help you experience the heart of this man who was called to such a daunting task.

MEMORY VERSE

"For My people have forgotten Me,
They burn incense to worthless gods
And they have stumbled from their ways,
From the ancient paths,
To walk in bypaths,
Not on a highway."

JEREMIAH 18:15

REVIEW IT!
The theme of Jeremiah is judgment, judgment, judgment.

JEREMIAH
[Jerusalem's Final Judgment]

DAY TWO

COMPLETE READ: Chapters 12–22
QUICK READ: Chapter 2

A CRUCIAL CHAPTER

INTERESTING!
The response of Jeremiah to God's call was not the "I will" of Isaiah or the "I won't" of Moses, but "I can't."

hypocrite, *n.* "One who plays a part on the stage; one who feigns to be other and better than he is; a false pretender to virtue or piety."[1]

Jesus was not afraid to confront the hypocrites of His day:

"Woe to you, scribes and Pharisees, hypocrites! For you clean the outside of the cup and of the dish, but inside they are full of robbery and self-indulgence." (Matthew 23:25)

"Woe to you, scribes and Pharisees, hypocrites! For you are like whitewashed tombs which on the outside appear beautiful, but inside they are full of dead men's bones and all uncleanness." (Matthew 23:27)

"You hypocrites, rightly did Isaiah prophesy of you:
'This people honors Me with their lips,
But their heart is far away from Me.
But in vain do they worship Me.'" (Matthew 15:7-9)

That one may smile, and smile, and be a villain.
—WILLIAM SHAKESPEARE, *Hamlet*

In a speech to the Harvard Law School Forum on February 16, 1999, actor Charlton Heston said, "I remember my son when he was five, explaining to his kindergarten class what his father did for a living. 'My daddy,' he said, 'pretends to be people.'"

DON'T MISS IT!
In one form or another,
the phrase *the Word
of the* LORD *came to
Jeremiah* occurs thirty-
three times in the book!

Actors are deliberate hypocrites. Their job requires them to pretend to be other people. Like actors, we sometimes play the part of another, pretending to be someone or something we are not. *This* kind of hypocrisy is not a job requirement!

Our Crucial Chapter for this week is Jeremiah 2, which is the prophet's first message to the people after receiving his call. It is a Crucial Chapter for a number of reasons. Not only is it Jeremiah's first speech of judgment, but it also is a classic illustration of how he spoke over and over again. It describes clearly how easy it is to move from true devotion to God to a disgusting hypocrisy. Follow the steps below as you move through Jeremiah 2:1–3:5.

1. Devotion to God (2:1-3): In your own words, describe the early devotion of the nation of Israel to God.

Hypocrisy can plunge the mind of a man into a dark abyss, when he believes his own self-flattery instead of God's verdict.

—JOHN CALVIN, sixteenth-century reformer and theologian

2. Desertion of God (2:4-19): Explain God's case against His people. Note the theme of "forsaking God."

3. Spiritual Adultery (2:20-28): As you record these depictions of spiritual adultery in your own words, also write down what you sense coming from God's heart. Remember these are His words: "Thus says the LORD" (2:2).

4. Spiritual Insensitivity (2:29-37): In what ways had the people of Judah shown their insensitivity, especially to God?

5. Spiritual Hypocrisy (3:1-5): Also read Jeremiah 7:1-11, which fleshes out this concept of hypocrisy even more. Summarize these passages in your own words.

Note the devastating path from initial devotion to God, to turning from God, to seeking other gods, to being insensitive to God's prodding to repent, and finally to faking a relationship with Him—hypocrisy.

What can you learn from this chapter's example of the road to hypocrisy? Has God shown you any potential areas of hypocrisy in your life?

MEMORY VERSE

"For My people have forgotten Me,
They burn incense to worthless gods
And they have stumbled from their ways,
From the ancient paths,
To walk in bypaths,
Not on a highway."

JEREMIAH 18:15

REVIEW IT!
Chapter 2 is our Crucial Chapter because it illustrates Jeremiah's messages and the road to hypocrisy.

JEREMIAH
[Jerusalem's Final Judgment]

INTERESTING!
God's pleas through Jeremiah for repentance by His people decrease dramatically as the book progresses: chapters 1–18: 14 times; chapters 19–36: 8 times; chapters 37–52: 1 time.

DAY THREE

COMPLETE READ: Chapters 23–32
QUICK READ: Chapter 36

A PROMINENT PLAYER

Our motto must continue to be perseverance. And ultimately I trust the Almighty will crown our efforts with success.

—WILLIAM WILBERFORCE, British antislavery activist and member of parliament

Clyde R. Hoey, governor of North Carolina from 1937–1941, once asked a country preacher in the Blue Ridge Mountains, "How many members are in your church?"

"Fifty," replied the pastor.

The governor knew numbers didn't always tell the story, so he asked, "How many are active?"

"Fifty," replied the pastor.

"Oh, you must be an unusual preacher," said Governor Hoey.

"Not necessarily," replied the pastor. "Twenty-five are active *for* me, and twenty-five are active *against* me."[2]

A 50 percent approval rating would have *thrilled* Jeremiah. Most of the time he experienced 0 percent approval. He preached for over forty years with virtually no positive response to his message—and yet he kept on.

In his commentary *Jeremiah*, Theo. Laetsch writes,

Unsparingly he pronounced God's judgments upon the impenitent without respect of persons. Like walls of brass he stood firm against frenzied prophets, fanatic priests, frantic people, furious kings. Calmly he faced this pack of snarling wolves ready to murder him. Neither defamation, nor persecution, nor imprisonment, nor threats of death kept him from speaking whatever God commanded him. Only when alone with himself and his God did he give voice to his agonized feelings, his doubts and fears, his heartaches and gnawing grief, his bitterness and his maledictions. And from every battle he rose more than a conqueror by the grace and power of Him who was the LORD, his Strength, his Fortress, and his Refuge in the day of affliction, because this LORD was Jehovah, his Righteousness.[3]

We will look at just a few passages describing the incredible difficulties Jeremiah faced in fulfilling his call from God. As you read these sections, summarize what took place.

11:18-23

20:1-6

26:10-15

36:1-26

37:11-16

Most of God's faithful
servants sooner or later
are called to endure
severe testing and trials.

38:1-13

What words would you use to describe how you would have felt had you been in Jeremiah's situation?

Jeremiah was only human and often reacted in typical human fashion. Briefly describe his reactions in the following passages.

12:1-4

20:7-10

*I had not then learned
to think of God as the
one great Circumstance
in whom we live
and move and have
our being, and of all
lesser circumstances
as necessarily the
kindest, wisest,
best, because either
ordered or permitted
by Him. Hence my
disappointment and
trial were very great.*

—J. HUDSON TAYLOR,
nineteenth-century
English missionary
to China

20:14-18

But in spite of these expressions of frustration, Jeremiah endured—for over forty years! Jeremiah 20:11-13 describes what kept him going. Meditate especially on the following phrases:

"But the LORD is with me." (20:11)

"Sing to the LORD, praise the LORD! (20:13)

"For He has delivered the soul of the needy one." (20:13)

How can these thoughts help you with difficulties God may be calling you to endure today?

Is there someone you know who is standing strong for God in spite of opposition? Use these Scriptures to pray for that person now.

MEMORY VERSE

"For My people have forgotten Me,
They burn incense to worthless gods
And they have stumbled from their ways,
From the ancient paths,
To walk in bypaths,
Not on a highway."

JEREMIAH 18:15

REVIEW IT!
Jeremiah is our Prominent Player because he modeled how to endure trials with honesty.

JEREMIAH
[Jerusalem's Final Judgment]

FACT
The prophet Jeremiah
is considered
one of the most
melancholy images in
Michelangelo's Sistine
Chapel fresco.

DAY FOUR

COMPLETE READ: Chapters 33–42
QUICK READ: Chapters 18–19

A NOTABLE FEATURE

In the book of Jeremiah we encounter a very human prophet, and a God who is alarmingly alive. Jeremiah makes it clear that no one chooses to fall into the hands of such a God. You are chosen, you resist, you resort to rage and bitterness and, finally, you succumb to the God who has given you your identity in the first place.

—KATHLEEN NORRIS, *THE CLOISTER WALK*

When we understand more about Jeremiah and his God, we see how appropriate and effective the metaphor in chapters 18 and 19 really is. The picture of the potter, his wheel, the clay, and the pot drives home the message of the sovereignty of God.

Read Jeremiah 18:1-3; then read the following by G. Christian Weiss from his book *Insights into Bible Times and Customs*:

God's people have always in their worst condition found out the best of their God.

—CHARLES SPURGEON, noted English Baptist minister

These wheels, as used today, are usually constructed of wood. They are solid, heavy, round devices, usually constructed by the potter himself. Each is composed of two wheels in horizontal positions. One is near the ground, at the lower end of a vertical axle, at the potter's foot, and the other is at the top, just a few inches above the level of his workbench or table. The upper wheel turns when the lower one is kicked into motion by the potter's foot. As the wheels are thus spun, the potter takes a lump of clay and puts it in the center of the upper wheel. As it spins, he forms the vessel with his palms and fingers. The thumb and the first two fingers of the right hand are generally used for the formation of the smaller vessels. In the making of larger vessels, both hands are used, one on the inside and the other on the outside, shaping the vessel according to the potter's design and skill.[4]

How often in our lives do *we* determine to be the potter—doing all we can to control and mold the world in which we live? But we are not the potter and will never be. We are simply the clay in God's masterful and merciful hands.

Now read 18:4 and then the following as Weiss continues:

This is not an unusual occurrence in the making of clay pottery. A malformation caused by some defect in the clay often develops in the vessel's wall as the clay speeds between the potter's fingers or hands. It might be a tiny stone that escaped the workman's attention during the preparation of the clay, or a chip of wood or piece of straw, or it may be nothing more than a small, hard bit of clay that had not yielded to the dampening and kneading process.

Sometimes when the potter's fingers strike the unyielding substance, his entire vessel collapses, and the beautiful pot or jar being formed suddenly becomes an unshapely mass of ugly clay! In these instances, the potter may brush the whole mass off the wheel and discard it, or he may add a bit of water to the mass of clay and carefully work it between his fingers until he finds and removes the unwanted particle. Then he will set his wheel into motion again and remake the vessel according to his design and purpose.[5]

BY THE NUMBERS
Jeremiah announced God's judgment as "by the sword" sixty-nine times, "by famine" thirty-one times, and "by pestilence" sixteen times.

No more colorful figure emerges from the pages of the Old Testament than the prophet Jeremiah. . . . Tragically he stood in the main stream of rushing humanity warning the heedless throng of the certain destruction awaiting them. Madly they rushed on into death and exile over the struggling form of the faithful messenger of God.

—KYLE M. YATES, *Preaching from the Prophets*

Now that you can picture what Jeremiah was seeing, read 18:5-12 and express in your own words the meaning of the potter metaphor.

In chapter 19 the pottery image is used again. Read and summarize this chapter. What were your feelings as you read what God told Jeremiah to do with the pot?

These two pictures in chapters 18 and 19 not only lend vivid color to God's message of judgment delivered through Jeremiah, but they also powerfully illustrate the sovereignty of God over all He has created—including man and woman. He is the sovereign Potter, fashioning each of us into the vessel He envisions.

As you consider your own life, list some specific ways in which God has shaped you into the person He wants you to be. Consider your family of origin, trials, training, successes, failures, personal relationships, gifts, talents, and so on. How do you feel about the vessel He is shaping? Honestly communicate your thoughts to God.

MEMORY VERSE

"For My people have forgotten Me,
They burn incense to worthless gods
And they have stumbled from their ways,
From the ancient paths,
To walk in bypaths,
Not on a highway."

JEREMIAH 18:15

REVIEW IT!
A Notable Feature of the book of Jeremiah is the metaphor of the potter because it gives insight into the sovereignty of God.

JEREMIAH
[Jerusalem's Final Judgment]

DAY FIVE

COMPLETE READ: Chapters 43–52
QUICK READ: Chapter 9

CHECK IT OUT
Jeremiah was a contemporary of the prophet Habakkuk.

A TIMELESS PRINCIPLE

Thus says the LORD, "Let not a wise man boast of his wisdom, and let not the mighty man boast of his might, let not a rich man boast of his riches." (Jeremiah 9:23)

Wisdom, might, and riches comprise a trinity of glitter in which many men glory and for which other men grasp. But in the words of the wisest man that ever lived, "Vanity of vanities! All is vanity" (Ecclesiastes 1:2).

Verses 23 and 24 of Jeremiah 9 are an oasis in a vast desert, a green garden in a desolate wilderness. Until these verses, sin and judgment pile higher and higher. But one bright truth cuts through the gloom and offers this worthwhile goal: "'But let him who boasts boast of this, that he understands and knows Me, that I am the LORD who exercises lovingkindness, justice and righteousness on earth; for I delight in these things,' declares the LORD" (9:24).

Think about verse 23 and respond to the following questions.

Wisdom itself is a good thing. But what do you suppose boasting in wisdom would look like?

Oh, the fullness, pleasure, sheer excitement of knowing God on earth!
—JIM ELLIOT, martyred American missionary

Might is certainly not bad. But what would boasting in might look like?

Riches are acceptable. But what would boasting in them look like?

Verse 24 contrasts verse 23. God's true desire for us as His children is that we understand and know Him. *To understand* is to have correct insight into the nature of a thing and to act in keeping with that understanding. It primarily involves the intellect and the will. *To know* includes the idea of understanding, with the addition of the emotions to the intellect and the will.

Describe what it means to you to know God (not to know *about* Him or *of* Him—but to know *Him*).

Father, give us wisdom to perceive You, intellect to understand You, diligence to seek You, patience to wait for You, eyes to behold You, a heart to meditate on You and a life to proclaim You.
—SAINT BENEDICT, first-century Italian monk

Briefly catalog the key points in your journey to knowing God. What were some defining moments? Who were some crucial people? Were there any "aha!" experiences?

Knowing God the way He wants to be known is the highest calling of our life. Is there a response you should make right now that might help you in this lifelong pursuit? Are you willing to verbalize that response to God?

What makes life worthwhile is having a big enough objective, something which catches our imagination and lays hold of our allegiance; and this the Christian has, in a way that no other way has. For what higher, more exalted, and more compelling goal can there be than to know God?

—J. I. PACKER, theologian, professor, and author of *Knowing God*

MEMORY VERSE

"For My people have forgotten Me,
They burn incense to worthless gods
And they have stumbled from their ways,
From the ancient paths,
To walk in bypaths,
Not on a highway."

JEREMIAH 18:15

JEREMIAH
[Jerusalem's Final Judgment]

REVIEW

1. The theme of Jeremiah is judgment, judgment, _____ .

2. Chapter 2 is our Crucial Chapter because it illustrates Jeremiah's messages and the road to _____ .

3. Jeremiah is our Prominent Player because he modeled how to endure trials with

   _____ .

4. A Notable Feature of the book of Jeremiah is the metaphor of the _____ because it gives insight into the sovereignty of God.

5. "'For my people have _____ Me,
   They burn incense to worthless gods
   And they have stumbled from their ways,
   From the ancient paths,
   To walk in bypaths,
   Not on a highway.'"

JEREMIAH 18:_____

LAMENTATIONS

[Jerusalem's Destruction Mourned]

The LORD's lovingkindnesses indeed never cease,

For His compassions never fail.

They are new every morning;

Great is Your faithfulness.

LAMENTATIONS 3:22-23

THREE

LAMENTATIONS
[Jerusalem's Destruction Mourned]

INTRODUCTION

The first five books in the prophetical section of the Old Testament are generally titled The Major Prophets. They are more accurately called The Major Prophetical Books because Lamentations is not a prophet. In reality, there are four major prophets who wrote five major prophetical books. Jeremiah wrote both the book by his name and this book, Lamentations.

The book of Lamentations is exactly what its title claims it to be—a series of laments. Picture Jeremiah, after forty years of sacrificial preaching, sitting near the gate of Jerusalem as the people he had warned (and who had ignored him) trudge toward exile in Babylonia.

This book is the prophet's lament over his fallen city and its inhabitants. It is a book of tears and grief. But even in the midst of despondency there is light. God is still faithful, and His mercies are still new and fresh every morning.

The words of a familiar hymn speak to this promise:

> *Great is Thy faithfulness, O God my Father!*
> *There is no shadow of turning with Thee;*
> *Thou changest not, Thy compassions, they fail not;*
> *As Thou hast been Thou forever will be.*[1]

Lamentations
[Jerusalem's Destruction Mourned]

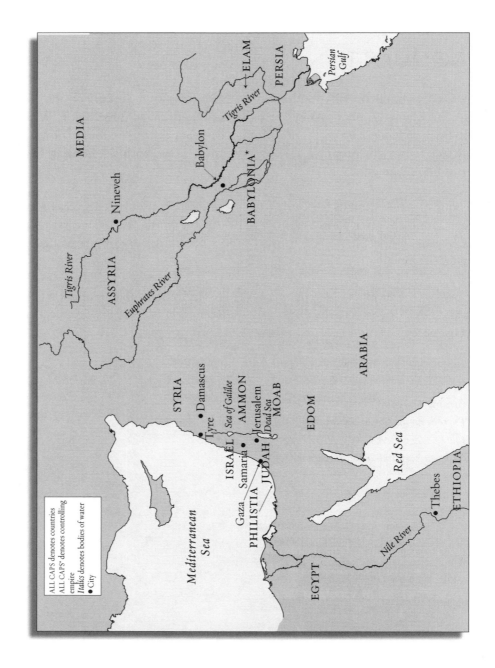

Lamentations
[Jerusalem's Destruction Mourned]

OVERVIEW

WHO: Author: The prophet Jeremiah, according to most scholars
Main Characters: Jeremiah and the people of Jerusalem

WHAT: Five poems of mourning over the destruction of Jerusalem and the temple at the hands of the Babylonians

WHEN: Probably written just after Jerusalem's destruction in 586 BC and before Jeremiah was taken captive to Egypt

WHERE: Jerusalem at the time of total devastation

WHY: To commemorate/remember the terrible destruction of Jerusalem

I.   JEREMIAH DESCRIBED JERUSALEM'S DESOLATION (LAMENTATIONS 1).

A. The city was _____ by its inhabitants and former friends.

B. The city was _____; nothing was as it was. There was no comfort.

II.   JEREMIAH DESCRIBED JERUSALEM'S DESTRUCTION (LAMENTATIONS 2).

A. In anger, the Lord _____ the city as a judgment.

1. God's hand of protection was removed.

2. God abandoned His temple.

3. God silenced the prophets and elders.

B. Jeremiah delivered a message of _____ to Jerusalem's unfaithful.

III.   JEREMIAH DESCRIBED HIS DESPAIR (LAMENTATIONS 3).

A. Jeremiah voiced feelings of personal _____ at what he saw.

B. Jeremiah expressed faith by declaring there was _____ for God's chosen.

IV. JEREMIAH DESCRIBED JERUSALEM'S DEFEAT (LAMENTATIONS 4).

A. Jeremiah witnessed the _____ of the city and relayed the conditions.

B. Jeremiah listed the _____ for Jerusalem's defeat.

C. Jeremiah prophesied the enemy's future _____ .

V. JEREMIAH DESCRIBED JERUSALEM'S DESPONDENCY (LAMENTATIONS 5).

A. Jeremiah _____ and _____ for the people in prayer.

B. Jeremiah _____ with God to intervene for His children.

APPLICATION

Obedience to God's Word brings blessing; disobedience brings judgment. God in His mercy offers opportunities for repentance, but when we refuse to repent, we will answer for our sin. Also, in the midst of every trial lies the hope of God's mercy and faithfulness, which is given to us anew each and every day.

LAMENTATIONS
[Jerusalem's Destruction Mourned]

LEARNING FOR LIFE

1. What happened in the book of Jeremiah (prophesied in Deuteronomy 28) that prompted the prophet Jeremiah to write the book of Lamentations?

2. What does Lamentations mean, and why is this title appropriate?

3. Describe some of what Jeremiah saw as he wrote about the devastation in Jerusalem.

4. Jeremiah wept over Jerusalem prior to and immediately after her fall to Babylonia. Who would weep over the city some six hundred years later? (See Matthew 23:37-38.)

5. Why did all this horror happen to God's chosen people and to the city that housed His temple?

6. Share a time when disobedience to God resulted in difficult consequences for you.

7. Have you ever lost your hope, only to be refreshed by remembering God's past faithfulness toward you? Tell about your experience.

LAMENTATIONS
[Jerusalem's Destruction Mourned]

DAY ONE

COMPLETE READ: Chapters 1–5
QUICK READ: Chapter 1

THE BIG PICTURE

> This pathetic little fivefold poem, the Lamentations, has been called "an elegy written in a graveyard." It is a cloudburst of grief, a river of tears, a sea of sobs.
>
> —J. SIDLOW BAXTER, *EXPLORE THE BOOK*

Babylonia destroyed the city of Jerusalem, just as Jeremiah had predicted. Judgment had finally come. The people were unconditionally defeated, stumbling away from their homes as captives of a foreign nation. Jeremiah had warned them over and over again; after their collapse, he mourned their plight in this short poem of grief, the book of Lamentations.

Give sorrow words: the grief that does not speak whispers the o'er-fraught heart, and bids it break.

—WILLIAM SHAKESPEARE, Macbeth

For forty years, he had warned the people to turn from their sin and to God. If they refused, he said, God would send a foreign invader to discipline them for their disobedience. They not only refused to respond to God's message, but they also persecuted the messenger. As a result, God's prediction came true. Babylonia came and Jerusalem fell.

The poet's lament is given in five sections, as shown in the chart on the next page.

The first four chapters are alphabetic acrostics. The first word of each of the twenty-two verses in chapters 1, 2, and 4 begins with one of the twenty-two letters of the Hebrew alphabet in a successive pattern. Thus, verse 1 begins with the equivalent of our

Jerusalem Deserted	Jerusalem Destroyed	Jeremiah Distressed	Jerusalem Defeated	Jerusalem Distressed
22-Verse Poem	22-Verse Poem	66-Verse Poem	22-Verse Poem	22-Verse Poem
1	2	3	4	5

DID YOU KNOW?
In the Hebrew Bible, Lamentations is grouped with Song of Solomon, Ruth, Esther, and Ecclesiastes rather than Isaiah, Jeremiah, Ezekiel, and Daniel.

letter A, verse 2 with the equivalent of B, and so forth. Chapter 3 has sixty-six verses, with each Hebrew letter introducing a group of three verses. Chapter 5 is not an acrostic poem.

There may be several reasons for Jeremiah's choice of this style. It fostered easier memorization; it made it difficult to edit, add, or rearrange any verse; it encouraged using the poem for liturgical purposes; and it expressed the full range of suffering, from beginning to end.

Most scholars believe Jeremiah wrote Lamentations, even though he is not mentioned by name. Many passages in the lament are clear reflections of similar thoughts and style in the book of Jeremiah. The writer of the book was clearly an eyewitness to the tragedy, as was Jeremiah. He likely wrote this dirge very soon after the fall of Jerusalem to Babylonia in 586 BC.

The English title for the book follows the Greek and Latin titles, which meant "dirge, laments, tears." The subtitle in Jerome's Vulgate, the fourth-century Latin version of the Bible, is The Lamentations of Jeremiah, which became the specific basis for the English title.

In your study of Jeremiah, you gained an appreciation for a man who remained faithful to God in spite of one of the most difficult ministries ever recorded. As you read the book of Lamentations, you will see yet another side of Jeremiah. You may want to keep a separate journal of things you learn about him as you read.

Grief is itself a medicine.

—WILLIAM COWPER, eighteenth-century hymn writer, poet, and translator

From this lesson's reading, jot down anything that made an impression on you.

O Truly, it is in darkness that one finds the light, so when we are in sorrow, then this light is nearest of all to us.

—MEISTER ECKHART, twelfth-century Christian mystic

REVIEW IT!
The theme of Lamentations is mourning for the fall of Jerusalem.

MEMORY VERSE

The LORD's lovingkindnesses indeed never cease,
For His compassions never fail.
They are new every morning;
Great is Your faithfulness.

LAMENTATIONS 3:22-23

LAMENTATIONS
[Jerusalem's Destruction Mourned]

DAY TWO

COMPLETE READ: Chapters 1–5
QUICK READ: Chapter 1

A CRUCIAL CHAPTER

Lamentations could be called the "funeral of a city." The book is a dirge about a devastating scene. Everything had been destroyed—the temple, the altars, the palace, the walls, and the gates. The few people left behind were in shock. Hopelessness filled the air.

Chapter 1 of this "funeral of a city" is our Crucial Chapter because it so graphically illustrates the utter destruction of the city and the sorrow of its people. The chapter is divided equally into two parts:

Lament by the Person of Jeremiah		Lament by the Personified Jerusalem	
1	11	12	22

If you haven't already read chapter 1, your Quick Read, do so now and then write down as many words or phrases as you can that describe how you felt as you read.

As the chart shows, verses 1-11 were written from the prophet's

WHAT'S IN A NAME?
One man subtitled the book of Lamentations *Wailing Without a Wall*.

Sorrow is knowledge: they who know the most must mourn the deepest.
—LORD BYRON, English poet and satirist

CHECK IT OUT
The word groan or
groaning occurs five
times in chapter 1.

perspective and verses 12-22 from the city's perspective. Review this chapter and write down your specific thoughts in response to the following questions.

What comparisons or similarities do you see between the two sections?

What contrasts or differences do you see between them? (Notice the pronoun changes from "she" and "her" in verses 1-11 to "me," "my," and "I" in verses 12-22.)

My early grief was mixed with so much shock it doesn't even count as grief. It took six months before the terror and panic stopped, and the welling sadness began.

—Vanessa Rappaport, American poet

The actual events mourned by Jeremiah in Lamentations are recorded in 2 Kings. Compare the following pairs of passages and describe what is portrayed by each pair.

LAMENTATIONS	YOUR DESCRIPTION	2 KINGS
1:11,19		25:3
1:10		25:13-15
1:5,18		25:11

The following verses all have one theme or phrase in common: 1:2,9,16,17,21. What is the common idea?

What is the impact of the repetition of this idea?

What are your personal thoughts or feelings as you finish this study?

MEMORY VERSE

The LORD's lovingkindnesses indeed never cease,
For His compassions never fail.
They are new every morning;
Great is Your faithfulness.

LAMENTATIONS 3:22-23

LAMENTATIONS
[Jerusalem's Destruction Mourned]

FACT
The Hebrew title
for this book comes
from the first word of
chapters 1, 2, and 4:
"Ah, how!"

DAY THREE

COMPLETE READ: Chapters 1–5
QUICK READ: Chapter 2

A PROMINENT PLAYER

Meditation is the activity of calling to mind, and thinking over, and dwelling on, and applying to oneself, the various things that one knows about the works and ways and purposes and promises of God. . . . Its purpose is to clear one's mental and spiritual vision of God, and to let His truth make its full and proper impact on one's mind and heart. It is a matter of talking to oneself about God and oneself; it is, indeed, often a matter of arguing with oneself, reasoning oneself out of moods of doubt and unbelief into a clear apprehension of God's power and grace.

—J. I. PACKER, *KNOWING GOD*

*Our ground of hope
is that God does not
weary of mankind.*
—RALPH W. SOCKMAN,
senior minister, Christ
Church, New York City

Most of us would never choose the book of Lamentations for meditation on "the works and ways and purposes and promises of God." It seems too full of wrath and hurt and pain and grief. To be sure, these themes dominate the book. But God has also woven threads of light into this fabric of darkness—threads of hope and encouragement.

God is surely the Prominent Player in this poem of lament. As you scan the book, look for words that complete the following phrases. Briefly jot down what you find, including the references.

The Lord is . . .

The Lord did or has done . . .

I ask the Lord . . .

As you meditate on these concepts, how would you describe:

God's character

God's feelings about sin

What God would have His people ask of Him

APPROPRIATE
In the original Hebrew, this book implements a "limping meter" because this melancholy rhythm was used in funeral dirges.

The only haven of safety is in the mercy of God, as manifested in Christ, in whom every part of our salvation is complete.
—JOHN CALVIN, Protestant reformer and theologian

As we meditate on God's character as it is revealed to us through the situation in Jerusalem thousands of years ago, the Holy Spirit is able to bridge the time gap and make the story relevant to our lives today. What do you sense God is saying to you about who He is and the role He wants to play in your life?

REVIEW IT!
The Prominent Player in this lament is God because of who He is and what He does.

MEMORY VERSE

The LORD's lovingkindnesses indeed never cease,
For His compassions never fail.
They are new every morning;
Great is Your faithfulness.

LAMENTATIONS 3:22-23

LAMENTATIONS
[Jerusalem's Destruction Mourned]

DAY FOUR

COMPLETE READ: Chapters 1–5
QUICK READ: Chapter 3

A NOTABLE FEATURE

In his book *The Bible Jesus Read*, Philip Yancey writes,

> Dan Allender, a Christian counselor, asks, To whom do you vocalize the most intense, irrational—meaning inchoate, inarticulate—anger? Would you do so with someone who could fire you or cast you out of a cherished position or relationship? Not likely. You don't trust them—you don't believe they would endure the depths of your disappointment, confusion. . . . The person who hears your lament and far more bears your lament against them, paradoxically, is someone you deeply, wildly trust. . . . The language of lament is oddly the shadow side of faith.[2]

In your Quick Read for today, Jeremiah certainly displayed disappointment and confusion. And he took these emotions straight to the only One who could handle and deal with them properly—the One in whom, in Allender's words, Jeremiah could "deeply, wildly trust." Jeremiah's honesty toward God in expressing his emotions is our Notable Feature of this book.

Jeremiah had been faithful to his call. He had preached; he had persevered; he had endured—all because God had commanded him to. Considering his message of judgment against the people of Judah, it's understandable that they would reject

COUNT 'EM
The words I, me, and my occur thirty-three times in Lamentations 3:1-18.

Silent sorrow is only the more fatal.
—JEAN BAPTISTE RACINE, French dramatist and poet

SOBERING
J. Vernon McGee
describes the book of
Lamentations as "a
hymn of heartbreak,
a psalm of sadness, a
symphony of sorrow."

him. But at times he felt that even God, who had given him the
message, was against him!

Chapter 3:1-18 records the prophet's complaint against God. As
you study these verses, respond to the two questions that follow.

What kind of imagery did Jeremiah use to describe what he felt
God had done to him? List as many examples as you can find.

Putting all these pictures together, describe in your own words
how Jeremiah felt about God's perceived treatment of him.

*These sad times we
must obey. Speak what
we feel, not what we
ought to say.*
—WILLIAM SHAKESPEARE,
King Lear

In verses 39-66, Jeremiah prayed to God, first on behalf of
his countrymen and then for himself. In which verse does this
switch take place? How do you know?

What are some examples of complaints in Jeremiah's prayer? How about requests?

We have not yet considered the crucial verses in the middle of this chapter, verses 19-38. We will study them as our Timeless Principle. However, from what you have studied so far in this chapter, what have you learned about handling disappointment, confusion, and even anger in your relationship with God?

Is there anything specific you need to do right now as a result of this study?

MEMORY VERSE

The LORD's lovingkindnesses indeed never cease,
For His compassions never fail.
They are new every morning;
Great is Your faithfulness.

LAMENTATIONS 3:22-23

REVIEW IT!
Our Notable Feature is Jeremiah's honest expression of disappointment, confusion, and even anger directed at God.

LAMENTATIONS
[Jerusalem's Destruction Mourned]

REMEMBER
Lamentations is the only prophetical book not named for a prophet.

DAY FIVE

COMPLETE READ: Chapters 1–5
QUICK READ: Chapter 3:19-38

A TIMELESS PRINCIPLE

Christian Reger spent four years as a prisoner at the Dachau concentration camp near Munich for nothing more than belonging to the Confessing Church, the branch of the German state church that opposed Hitler. Later, as a leader of the International Dachau Committee, Reger returned to the grounds in order to restore the camp as a monument that the world can't forget. "[Friedrich] Nietzsche said a man can undergo torture if he knows the why of his life," Reger told author Philip Yancey. "But I, here at Dachau, learned something far greater. I learned to know the Who of my life. He was enough to sustain me then, and is enough to sustain me still."

—JAMES EMERY WHITE, *LIFE-DEFINING MOMENTS*

Man may dismiss compassion from his heart, but God never will.

—WILLIAM COWPER, eighteenth-century hymn writer, poet, and translator

The truth expressed by Christian Reger echoes the words of Jeremiah in Lamentations 3:19-25:

> Remember my affliction and my wandering,
>   the wormwood and bitterness.
> Surely my soul remembers
> And is bowed down within me.
> This I recall to my mind,
> Therefore I have hope.

The LORD's lovingkindnesses indeed never cease,
For His compassions never fail.
They are new every morning;
Great is Your faithfulness.
"The LORD is my portion," says my soul,
"Therefore I have hope in Him."
The LORD is good to those who wait for Him,
To the person who seeks Him.

NOTE
Jeremiah is the only writing prophet with two books in the Old Testament.

As you meditate on the Timeless Principle, "Great Is Your Faithfulness," and the other encouraging statements about God in these verses, write down specific instances of trial and difficulty in which you experienced the power of these great truths.

Which phrase in verses 19-25 made the greatest impact on you? Why?

Best of all is, God is with us.
—JOHN WESLEY, eighteenth-century founder of Methodism

We tend to think of these great truths about God only when we are in distress. But His great faithfulness, His compassions that are new every morning, and His lovingkindnesses that never cease are just as true and real and necessary for the ordinary days of our lives as for the extraordinarily stressful ones. Interestingly, one of the greatest hymns ever written about the faithfulness of God was penned out of mostly ordinary circumstances.

CONSIDER
If ever a person could
be excused for saying,
"I told you so!" it
would be Jeremiah.

Kenneth W. Osbeck writes this about Thomas Obadiah Chisholm's hymn "Great Is Thy Faithfulness": "While many hymns are born out of a particular dramatic experience, this hymn was simply the result of the author's 'morning by morning realization of God's personal faithfulness.'"[3]

In the space that follows, write down some of the normal, not-so-dramatic displays of God's great faithfulness to you.

You may want to use the words of Chisholm's hymn to voice your thanksgiving to God for His great faithfulness:

Just as the body wears clothes and the flesh skin, and the bones flesh, and the heart the chest, so we, soul and body are clothed and enfolded in the goodness of God.

—JULIAN OF NORWICH, twelfth-century religious mystic

> *Great is Thy faithfulness, O God my Father!*
> *There is no shadow of turning with Thee;*
> *Thou changest not, Thy compassions, they fail not;*
> *As Thou hast been Thou forever will be.*
>
> *Summer and winter, and springtime and harvest,*
> *Sun, moon and stars in their courses above,*
> *Join with all nature in manifold witness*
> *To Thy great faithfulness, mercy and love.*
>
> *Pardon for sin and a peace that endureth,*
> *Thine own dear presence to cheer and to guide,*
> *Strength for today and bright hope for tomorrow—*
> *Blessings all mine, with ten thousand beside!*

Great is Thy faithfulness! Great is Thy faithfulness!
Morning by morning new mercies I see;
All I have needed Thy hand hath provided—
Great is Thy faithfulness, Lord, unto Me![4]

MEMORY VERSE

The LORD's lovingkindnesses indeed never cease,
For His compassions never fail.
They are new every morning;
Great is Your faithfulness.

LAMENTATIONS 3:22-23

LAMENTATIONS
[Jerusalem's Destruction Mourned]

REVIEW

1. The theme of Lamentations is mourning the fall of _____ .

2. Chapter 1 is our Crucial Chapter because it so graphically illustrates the utter _____ of the city and the sorrow of its people.

3. The Prominent Player in this lament is _____ , in who He is and what He does.

4. Our Notable Feature is Jeremiah's _____ expression of disappointment, confusion, and even anger directed at God.

5. "The LORD's _____ indeed never cease,

    For His compassions never fail.

    They are new every morning;

    Great is Your faithfulness."

LAMENTATIONS 3:_____ - _____

EZEKIEL

[Israel's Eventual Restoration]

Then the Spirit lifted me up, and I heard a great

rumbling sound behind me, "Blessed be the glory

of the LORD in His place."

 EZEKIEL 3:12

FOUR

EZEKIEL
[Israel's Eventual Restoration]

INTRODUCTION

Together, The Major Prophets portray a God who is stunning and spectacular. Isaiah introduces us to the Incomparable One who will stand no rivals. Jeremiah describes the Righteous One who judges sin. The book of Lamentations portrays the Faithful One who will provide new mercies every morning. As we will see next week, Daniel dramatically represents the Sovereign One who controls all of history. And this week we will see Ezekiel exalt the Glorious One who displays His glory in all He does.

Some parts of Ezekiel are mysterious, some are confusing, and others seem beyond our ability to grasp. And yet in all of this, the power, majesty, and glory of God shine like the noonday sun. It is God's desire that all people recognize and bow before His glory.

Ezekiel writes to a people entrenched in exile a message transcending time and space. It is first a message of judgment, but then of firm hope, rooted in the unsurpassed glory of God.

During this study, you may find yourself struggling to understand God in an entirely new way or to trust Him on a whole new level. Enjoy the encounter!

Ezekiel
[Israel's Eventual Restoration]

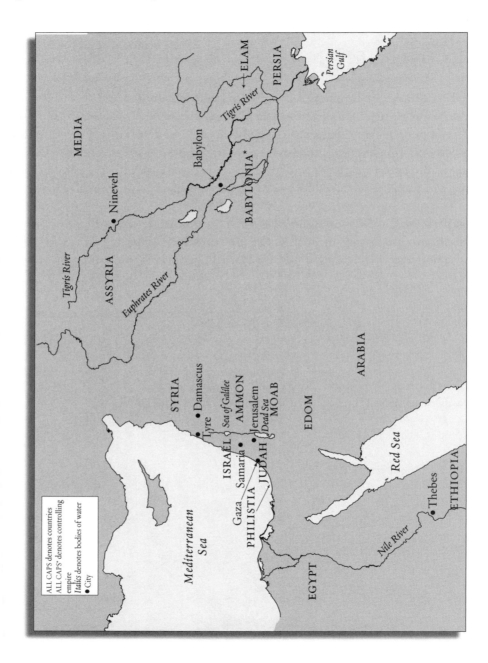

E ZEKIEL
[Israel's Eventual Restoration]

OVERVIEW

WHO: Author: Ezekiel, a priest and prophet to the Jewish exiles in Babylonia

WHAT: Ezekiel preached condemnation (chapters 1–32) and consolation (chapters 33–48) to Judah so that all people would know that God is the Sovereign Lord

WHEN: Ezekiel was probably born in 622 BC, was deported to Babylonia in 597 BC, prophesied from 592 until 570 BC, finished this book in 565 BC, and died around 560 BC

WHERE: Ezekiel began his ministry at age thirty in Tel-Abib, a Jewish colony

WHY: God used Ezekiel as a sign to warn His people in captivity and remind them of the reason for their misfortunes

I.   THE HISTORY OF JUDAH

A. Judah was _____ three times in twenty years by Babylon.

   1. The _____ exile in 605 BC, Babylon deported Daniel.

   2. The _____ exile in 597 BC, Babylon deported King Jehoiakim and ten thousand others.

   3. The _____ and final exile in 586 BC, Babylon deported the rest of the educated people and completely destroyed the temple and the city of Jerusalem.

B. The book of Ezekiel took place and was written before, during, and after the third and final exile.

   1. _____ was the supreme world power at that time.

   2. _____ was the ruler of Babylon.

   3. The young, godly prophet _____ was already in a position of power and influence in the Babylonian court.

II. THE HISTORY OF EZEKIEL (EZEKIEL 1–3)

A. Ezekiel spent his youth in _____ .

   1. Ezekiel was trained as a _____ .

   2. Ezekiel was probably a pupil of the godly prophet _____ .

   3. Ezekiel was about seventeen during the _____ exile.

B. Ezekiel was deported during the _____ exile around the age of twenty-five.

   1. Ezekiel lived in an area near Tel-Abib, a _____ colony.

   2. Ezekiel ministered to the _____ in captivity for twenty-two years.

   3. Ezekiel prophesied through _____ (also: symbols, poetry, proverbs, and parables).

III. THE JUDGMENT ON JUDAH (EZEKIEL 4–24)

A. Ezekiel prophesied about the third exile and the destruction of the _____ and the city.

B. Ezekiel preached that God's _____ would depart from the temple and the area of Judah.

C. Ezekiel warned the people to _____ to God if they wanted to _____ to Jerusalem.

IV. THE JUDGMENT ON OTHER NATIONS (EZEKIEL 25–32)

A. Ezekiel prophesied judgment against Israel's cruel _____ .

B. Ezekiel prophesied judgment against the great _____ of the day.

V. THE RESTORATION OF JUDAH (EZEKIEL 33–48)

    A. Ezekiel assured the people that God's _____ was sure.

    B. Ezekiel told the people that God would give them a _____ heart, spirit, and beginning.

    C. Ezekiel gave the people specific instructions on _____ the temple and the city.

APPLICATION

First Corinthians 6:19-20 says if you believe in Christ Jesus, your body is God's holy temple. Do you radiate His glory? If not, why not?

EZEKIEL
[Israel's Eventual Restoration]

LEARNING FOR LIFE

1. Review each book of The Major Prophets and its Timeless Principle.

2. What did you find interesting about Ezekiel, the man?

3. Why is the timing of Ezekiel's ministry important to know and understand?

4. Why did God judge Judah? What does that mean to you?

5. Why did God judge the other nations? How do God's sure judgment and the promise of restoration show His love to His people?

EZEKIEL
[Israel's Eventual Restoration]

DAY ONE

COMPLETE READ: Chapters 1—12
QUICK READ: Chapters 2 and 6

INTERESTING!
Ezekiel and Daniel
both lived in Babylonia
and were about the
same age.

THE BIG PICTURE

Sometimes we shy away from the unfamiliar, and for many, Ezekiel is an unfamiliar book. But if we shy away from it, assuming it is too difficult or irrelevant, we will miss an incredible portrayal of God. In order to understand it, though, we must first consider the historical context of Ezekiel's message: the destruction of Jerusalem and the exile of its people to Babylonia.

Babylonia destroyed Jerusalem and exiled its inhabitants in three stages. In 605 BC, hostages, including Daniel, were taken. In 597 BC, ten thousand more were carried off, including Ezekiel. And in 586 BC, the final destruction and exile took place.

Ezekiel had been in exile for five years before he uttered his first prophecies at the age of thirty (Ezekiel 1:1). From 592 to 586 BC, he proclaimed the coming destruction of the city of Jerusalem to the exiles already in Babylonia. Simultaneously, Jeremiah was preaching the same message to the citizens of Jerusalem.

Like Jeremiah, Ezekiel was a priest (1:3). Informed by his priestly background, he wrote in detail about the temple, the priests, and the offerings that would one day be resumed when Israel was gathered again.

The date of Ezekiel's last prophecy was 570 BC (29:17). He ministered to his fellow exiles for twenty-two years.

Because Ezekiel went into exile in Babylonia eleven years before the final destruction of Jerusalem and actually began his

Living is death; dying is life. We are not what we appear to be. On this side of the grave we are exiles, on that citizens; on this side orphans, on that children.

—HENRY WARD BEECHER, U.S. abolitionist and clergyman

NOTE
Ezekiel, Jeremiah,
and Zechariah were
the only three writing
prophets who were
also priests.

prophetic ministry six years before this devastating event, the majority of his prophecy (chapters 1–32) is a grim forecast of the city's destruction. But as the following chart shows, in chapters 33–48 the focus changes. As the prophet looked to the future, he saw hope. He knew that God would one day restore Jerusalem and once again meet His people in the temple to receive their worship.

592–587 BC	586 BC	585–570 BC
Judgment on JUDAH	Judgment on the NATIONS	Restoration of JUDAH
BEFORE the Fall of Jerusalem	DURING the Fall of Jerusalem	AFTER the Fall of Jerusalem
1 24	25 32	33 48

Whether his message was one of judgment or hope, Ezekiel was consumed by one passion: holding God's glory constantly before the people. Nearly seventy times he quoted God as saying, "They will know that I am the LORD." As you read this week, consider keeping a record of each of these occurrences with a short phrase explaining its impact.

What impressed you the most about your reading for today?

If it were not for hopes, the heart would break.

—THOMAS FULLER, seventeenth-century English clergyman

What was the most unique thing you read?

What do you need to ask God for as you begin this study?

MEMORY VERSE

Then the Spirit lifted me up, and I heard a great rumbling sound behind me, "Blessed be the glory of the LORD in His place."

EZEKIEL 3:12

REVIEW IT!
The theme of Ezekiel
is the glory of God
through judgment and
restoration.

EZEKIEL
[Israel's Eventual Restoration]

INTERESTING!
Ezekiel's ministry
occurred about the
same time money was
first coined in Rome.

DAY TWO

COMPLETE READ: Chapters 13–24
QUICK READ: Chapter 1

A CRUCIAL CHAPTER

> Ezekiel has been called "the Patmos-seer of the Old Testament." As to the exiled John on the island of Patmos, so to the exiled Ezekiel by the river Chebar, extraordinary visions were given.
>
> —J. SIDLOW BAXTER, *EXPLORE THE BOOK*

Our Crucial Chapter is certainly one of those extraordinary visions. Chapter 1 introduces us to sights and sounds seemingly better suited to the world of science fiction than of faith. But Ezekiel's vision was not fiction. It was the divine revelation of God, given to show His splendor, majesty, and glory. We, in turn, are amazed, astonished, and inspired to reverence and worship—exactly where humans should be in the presence of an eternal, holy, and awesome God.

After you have read chapter 1, write down words and phrases that describe the thoughts and feelings you had as you read.

The radiance of the divine beauty is wholly inexpressible; words cannot describe it, nor the ear grasp it.

—ABBA PHILIMON, first-century church father

Because the theme of Ezekiel is the glory of God, it is fitting for such a chapter to introduce the book. In your own words describe how this chapter illustrates the glory of God.

IT'S A MYSTERY
The location of the river Chebar (Ezekiel 1:3) has never been determined.

Bible interpreters have spent countless hours trying to unravel the symbolism of this vision in order to determine its meaning. Suggestions are numerous, but many scholars agree on a few broad themes or concepts. Search the chapter to find words, phrases, or verses that support the two themes listed below and write them in the spaces that follow.

1. An approaching judgment is pictured.

2. The events symbolized are under the control of heaven.

Men are never duly touched and impressed with a conviction of their insignificance until they have contrasted themselves with the majesty of God.
—JOHN CALVIN, sixteenth-century reformer and theologian

As Ezekiel recorded this vision, he was trying to describe clearly what he had seen. Note the times that he used words such as *resembling* and *something like*.

Do not be discouraged if you were confused when you began this chapter. Confusion often partners with awe—and awe can lead us to higher thoughts of God. If you had thoughts of "confused awe" as you read, jot them down here.

Now turn these thoughts into an appropriate prayer to your awesome and glorious God.

MEMORY VERSE

Then the Spirit lifted me up, and I heard a great rumbling sound behind me, "Blessed be the glory of the LORD in His place."

EZEKIEL 3:12

REVIEW IT!
Chapter 1 is a Crucial Chapter because it introduces the theme of the glory of God.

EZEKIEL
[Israel's Eventual Restoration]

DAY THREE

COMPLETE READ: Chapters 25–32
QUICK READ: Chapters 2–3

A PROMINENT PLAYER

In his book *The Call*, Os Guinness quotes Søren Kierkegaard, the nineteenth-century Danish philosopher, who wrote in his journal:

> The thing is to understand myself, to see what God really wants me to do; the thing is to find a truth which is true for me, to find the idea for which I can live and die.[1]

Guinness himself then goes on to say that "calling is the truth that God calls us to Himself so decisively that everything we are, everything we do, and everything we have is invested with a special devotion and dynamism lived out as a response to his summons and service."[2]

Your Quick Read for today is chapters 2–3, which gives a description of our Prominent Player Ezekiel's call to ministry by God. The vision in chapter 1 certainly got his attention. Then he heard the instruction this awesome God of the vision had for him. After reading chapters 2 and 3, go back and reread both the Kierkegaard and Guinness quotes above.

In your own words, relate the call of Ezekiel to the concepts in each of the quotes.

Vocation does not mean a goal that I pursue. It means a calling that I hear.
—PARKER J. PALMER, professor and author of *Let Your Life Speak*

Kierkegaard's quote

Guinness's quote

IMPORTANT
Ezekiel is in the line
of Eleazar, the son of
Aaron.

List the commands God gave Ezekiel in these chapters. Write
down the reference and a brief summary of each command.

State as succinctly as you can what you understand Ezekiel's
call to have been.

Put yourself in Ezekiel's sandals and try to think and feel as he
might have. What would you have understood readily?

*The place God calls
you to is the place
where your deep
gladness and the
world's deep hunger
meet.*

—FREDERICK BUECHNER,
author and novelist

110   EZEKIEL: DAY THREE

What would have baffled you?

What would have encouraged you?

Moses had his burning bush encounter. Isaiah had his "holy, holy, holy" vision. Paul had his Damascus Road experience. And Ezekiel had his four wheels vision. All of them were extraordinary "call" experiences. Most of us do not see burning bushes, lights from heaven, or visions. Instead, we hear our call through a still, small voice; an affirmation from others; a word from Scripture; a sense of God's leading; or one of many other means.

However you have sensed it, what do you believe to be your call for this life—the thing God really wants you to do (Kierkegaard) and that which you invest with "a special devotion and dynamism" (Guinness)? If you can, write it down. If you are uncertain of it, consider making your calling a matter of prayer in the days and weeks ahead.

> *God speaks to every individual through what happens to them moment by moment. The events of each moment are stamped with the will of God. If we have abandoned ourselves to God, there is only one rule for us: the duty of the present moment.*
>
> —JEAN-PIERRE DE CAUSSADE, eighteenth-century Jesuit priest

MEMORY VERSE

Then the Spirit lifted me up, and I heard a great rumbling sound behind me, "Blessed be the glory of the LORD in His place."

EZEKIEL 3:12

REVIEW IT!
Ezekiel is our Prominent Player because his prophecy is the carrying out of a call by God.

EZEKIEL
[Israel's Eventual Restoration]

DID YOU KNOW?
Ezekiel 37 is the source
of the familiar spiritual
with the lyrics: "leg
bone connected to the
ankle bone; ankle bone
connected to the foot
bone . . . now hear the
Word of the Lord!"

DAY FOUR

COMPLETE READ: Chapters 33–40
QUICK READ: Chapters 4 and 12

A NOTABLE FEATURE

Ezekiel's style of communication is more varied and picturesque
than any of the other prophets and is a Notable Feature of this
book. Here is a summary of the different modes Ezekiel used to
impress God's truth on his listeners:

Judgment on JUDAH	Judgment on the NATIONS	Restoration of JUDAH
9 Signs 8 Sermons 7 Parables 3 Visions	13 Sermons	1 Sign 2 Visions
1 24	25 32	33 48

*A picture has been
said to be something
between a thing and a
thought.*

—SAMUEL PALMER,
eighteenth-century
painter

It is said that a picture is worth a thousand words. And God
certainly proved that when He instructed Ezekiel to communicate using more than mere words. Ezekiel's ten signs and seven
parables are certainly worth more than a thousand words. For
example, the sign in Ezekiel 4:1-3 is a picture and prediction of
the destruction God would bring on Jerusalem.

As you read the following passages, describe in your own words
what the various signs were portraying and predicting.

4:4-8

4:9-17

12:1-16

12:17-20

37:15-23

QUESTION
If you were Ezekiel,
how readily would you
have carried out the
signs God instructed
you to perform?

In chapter 15, we find one of the parables in Ezekiel. Explain in your own words the point of the parable.

I dream my painting, and then I paint my dream.
—Vincent van Gogh, Dutch painter

Six hundred years later, the greatest Communicator ever also ministered through signs and parables—pictures of truths He wanted His hearers to understand, such as turning water to wine, cursing a fig tree so it withered, teaching about the

Vine and the branches, and washing His disciples' feet. As you look back on your walk with God, what "picture" from the Scriptures has made a deep and lasting impression on your life?

Take time to thank God for communicating to us in ways that are vivid and memorable.

REVIEW IT!
A Notable Feature in Ezekiel is his visualization of the message.

MEMORY VERSE

Then the Spirit lifted me up, and I heard a great rumbling sound behind me, "Blessed be the glory of the LORD in His place."

EZEKIEL 3:12

EZEKIEL
[Israel's Eventual Restoration]

DAY FIVE

COMPLETE READ: Chapters 41–45
QUICK READ: Chapter 20

CHECK IT OUT
God says, "I will"
twenty-three times in
chapter 36.

A TIMELESS PRINCIPLE

Years ago on the first Sunday in January, Minneapolis pastor John Piper preached a sermon on God's greatness and holiness from Isaiah 6. He did his best to hold up the majesty and glory of God before his people that Sunday morning but did not offer one word of life application. He had some concern about that because he knew that applying biblical truth to life is normally essential. Some weeks later a man took Piper aside to tell him that a few months earlier, he and his wife had discovered that their child was being sexually abused by a close relative. The father then said, "John, these have been the hardest months of our lives. Do you know what has gotten me through? The vision of the greatness of God's holiness that you gave me the first week of January. It has been the rock we could stand on."[3]

Piper writes,

> People are starving for the greatness of God. But most of them would not give this diagnosis of their troubled lives. The majesty of God is an unknown cure. There are far more popular prescriptions on the market, but the benefit of any other remedy is brief and shallow. Preaching that does not have the aroma of God's greatness may entertain for a season, but it will not touch the hidden cry of the soul: "Show me thy glory!"[4]

Ezekiel is all about the glory of God. Chapters 1–3 show God's

Knowing God. Is there any greater theme? Is there any nobler goal? Is there any greater good? Is there any deeper longing in the human heart?

—J. I. PACKER, theologian, professor, and author of *Knowing God*

COMPARE
Both Ezekiel 15 and John 15 contain parables about the vine.

heavenly glory. Chapters 4–39 describe how He gradually and reluctantly withdrew His glory from Israel because of the people's sin. Finally, chapters 40–48 paint the return of God's glory following the people's restoration. The glory of God is the theme of Ezekiel. Our Timeless Principle is "Know that I am the Lord"—a phrase that occurs over and over in the book of Ezekiel. (You'll find some occurrences of this phrase in your Quick Read for today.)

In both the display and the withdrawal of His glory, God seems to shout to His people, "I am the Lord! I want you to know Me intimately, deeply, faithfully!"

When you think of the glory of God, what images cross your mind?

The first and most important thing we know about God is that we know nothing about him except what He makes known.

—EMIL BRUNNER, Swiss theologian of the twentieth century

When you hear the words, "Know that I am the Lord," what thoughts do you have?

What correlations do you see between your thoughts and the experience of the father in the opening story? Do you believe that people today are "starving for the greatness of God"? Why or why not?

Summarize what God has revealed to you this week and how it could affect your walk with Him.

Close this lesson by turning these thoughts into a prayer.

MEMORY VERSE

Then the Spirit lifted me up, and I heard a great rumbling sound behind me, "Blessed be the glory of the LORD in His place."

EZEKIEL 3:12

EZEKIEL
[Israel's Eventual Restoration]

REVIEW

1. The theme of Ezekiel is the glory of God through judgment
   and _____ .

2. Chapter 1 is a Crucial Chapter because it introduces the theme of
   the _____ of God.

3. Ezekiel is our Prominent Player because his _____ is the carrying
   out of a call by God.

4. A Notable Feature in Ezekiel is his _____ of the message.

5. "Then the _____ lifted me up, and I heard a great rumbling sound
   behind me, 'Blessed be the glory of the LORD in His place.'"

   EZEKIEL 3:_____

DANIEL

[God's Supremacy over Nations]

Let the name of God be blessed forever and ever,

For wisdom and power belong to Him.

DANIEL 2:20

FIVE

DANIEL
[God's Supremacy over Nations]

INTRODUCTION

We conclude The Major Prophets with Daniel, a prophet whose book contains truth so mysterious and historically technical that scholars still cannot agree on all of its meaning and yet at the same time contains stories so simple and compelling that at least two of them are easily understood by children: Daniel in the lions' den and Daniel's three friends in the fiery furnace.

If you like the complexity of detailed and far-reaching prophecy, this book is for you. If you identify with the reality of suspense in personal experiences, you'll enjoy this book as well.

The common denominator through each verse of this exciting book is faith. Faith in the God who controls all of history—past, present, and future—and faith in the God who controls all of our experiences.

Look forward to your faith being challenged and strengthened as you observe how Daniel dealt with the complexity and reality of his life by submitting to and depending on our faithful God.

DANIEL
[God's Supremacy over Nations]

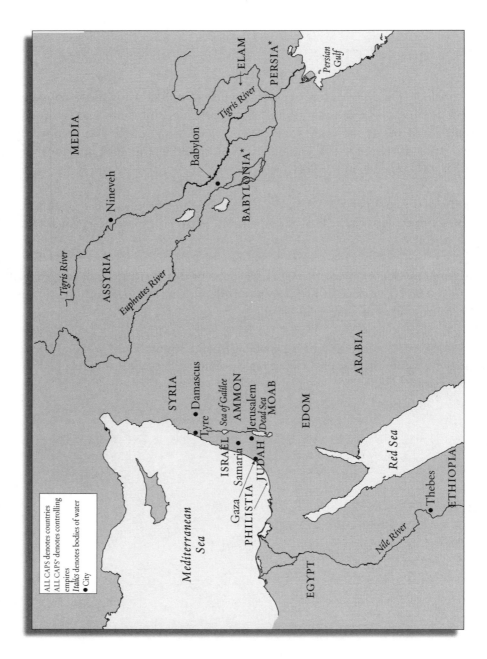

DANIEL
[God's Supremacy over Nations]

OVERVIEW

WHO: Author: Daniel
              Main Characters: Daniel, Meshach, Shadrach, Abednego, King Nebuchadnezzar

WHAT: History of Daniel's life and prophecies of Israel's and the Gentiles' future

WHEN: 605–536 BC

WHERE: Babylonia during the captivity

WHY: To show God's sovereignty over world history

I. **PERSONAL HISTORY OF DANIEL (DANIEL 1–6)**

  A. Daniel and his friends refused Babylon's food to keep God's dietary laws.

      1. Result: God gave them health, wisdom, and _____ .

      2. Lesson: Trusting the Sovereign God brings God's _____ .

  B. Daniel interpreted Nebuchadnezzar's first dream:

      1. Dream: A _____ with gold head, silver chest, bronze thighs, iron legs, iron/clay feet

      2. Interpretation: There would be four future Gentile _____ .

  C. Daniel's three friends refused to worship Nebuchadnezzar's image.

      1. Result: All three were thrown into the fiery _____ .

      2. Lesson: Trusting the Sovereign God brings God's _____ .

  D. Daniel interpreted Nebuchadnezzar's second dream:

      1. Dream: A _____ chopped down leaving a stump

      2. Interpretation: Nebuchadnezzar was the tree. He would be cut down by insanity until he repented of _____ .

E. Daniel interpreted God's message at King Belshazzar's feast:

1. Message: A hand _____ on the wall

2. Interpretation: Belshazzar's kingdom would _____ .
   That very night Belshazzar died.

F. Daniel refused King Darius's order not to petition any god but him.

1. Result: Daniel was thrown into the _____ den.

2. Lesson: Trusting the Sovereign God brings God's _____ .

II. UNIVERSAL PROPHECIES OF DANIEL (DANIEL 7–12)

A. Vision of Four Great Beasts

1. The beasts are the four future _____ kingdoms.

2. The fourth kingdom ruler who wages war with the saints is the
   _____ .

B. Vision of a Ram and Goat

1. The ram with two horns pictures the Medes-_____ .

2. The goat has one horn and pictures the _____ . The
   goat would defeat the ram (the Greeks defeated the Persians).

3. Chapter 8 is history (second and third kingdoms).

C. Vision of 70 Weeks

1. To the Jews, a "week" meant _____ . In 70 weeks (70 x 7
   years) or 490 years, God would deal with sin of Israel.

2. From decree to rebuild wall of Jerusalem there would be 7 weeks (7 x 7
   years) or 49 years until the wall was complete.

3. After an additional 62 weeks (7 weeks + 62 weeks = 69 weeks x 7 years) or
   483 years, _____ would come.

4. There is one prophetic week (7 years) left!

D. Vision of the Last "Week" and "Prince to Come"

    1. The "prince to come" (Antichrist) would make a covenant for 1 week (7 years) but after 3 ½ years would bring in abominations.

    2. There would be a time of _____ unlike the nation of Israel had ever known.

    3. The outcome: People will make a decision—for God or against God.

APPLICATION

As the fulfillment of the last seven years of history draws near, will you be a "Daniel" who stands firm in the face of opposition, trusts in trials, and believes God is sovereign over the future, thereby leading many to righteousness?

DANIEL
[God's Supremacy over Nations]

LEARNING FOR LIFE

1. Review the theme of each of the five major prophets.

2. Describe Daniel. What do you admire the most about him?

3. Which event in Daniel's life touched you the most? Why?

4. Describe one prophecy from this book that has yet to be fulfilled.

5. Daniel 2:34-35 describes a stone "cut out without hands" that destroyed an idol of iron, clay, bronze, silver, and gold. First Peter 2:4-8 speaks of another "stone"—this one living, chosen, and precious. Who is the "stone" in 1 Peter?

6. What did you learn about God from the book of Daniel?

7. What does the fact that God is sovereign over history mean to you personally?

DANIEL
[God's Supremacy over Nations]

DAY ONE

COMPLETE READ: Chapters 1–3
QUICK READ: Chapter 1

WHAT'S IN A NAME?
Daniel's name
was changed to
Belteshazzar, extolling
Bel, one of the gods
of the Babylonian
pantheon.

THE BIG PICTURE

Daniel is a book of visions and prophecies. When Ezekiel was taken into exile to Babylonia eleven years before Jerusalem fell, Daniel had already been there for nine years. When he arrived there as a young man, he was immediately put to the test. Refusing to eat King Nebuchadnezzar's food, Daniel had to rely on God to nurture and protect him. This was only the first of many tests of faith to come.

When Nebuchadnezzar's wise men could not interpret the king's dreams, God arranged for Daniel to be given the opportunity to interpret. What he saw was startling. Babylonia would be replaced as a world power by another country. That country would eventually be replaced by another, and then that one by still another. The three countries would be Medo-Persia, Greece, and Rome.

The book of Daniel stands Mount Everest-like in its prophetic detail: In chapter 9, the precise date of Jesus' death was predicted over six hundred years before it took place. The book of Daniel is a book of the future and of faith.

We can divide this book into two equal sections:

Personal History	Universal Prophecies
Fiery Furnace Handwriting on the Wall Lions' Den	Vision of 4 Beasts Vision of 2 Beasts Prayer and Answer
1 6	7 12

*Never be afraid to trust
an unknown future to
a known God.*

—CORRIE TEN BOOM,
Dutch Holocaust
survivor and author

The prophecies in this book are important and spectacular but difficult to interpret. Because of the time and space required to tackle them and considering the purpose of this study, we will focus primarily on the personal aspects of the book.

Daniel means "God is my judge," and the book is named after the author and main character. Daniel claimed to write the book (Daniel 12:4), and Christ attributed a quote from Daniel 9:27 to "Daniel the prophet" (see Matthew 24:15).

At age sixteen, Daniel was taken into captivity in Babylonia when King Nebuchadnezzar subdued Jerusalem in 605 BC. He ministered as a prophet and served as a government official during the reigns of Babylonian kings Nebuchadnezzar and Belshazzar and Persian kings Darius and Cyrus. He ministered at least until 536 BC, when he was eighty-five years old.

Daniel wrote to encourage his fellow Jewish exiles that all was not lost. Yes, they were removed from their homeland with little hope of return, but Daniel reminded them that God was still in control and orchestrating history to carry out His perfect plan—a plan that included the coming of the Messiah and the restoration of the Messiah's people, the Jews.

The sovereignty of God over earthly affairs is a theme that surfaces repeatedly in the book of Daniel. As you read, consider keeping a separate journal for evidence of this truth, listing each reference along with a brief statement describing what you see.

Begin by reviewing either today's Complete or Quick Read and jotting down any illustrations you find of God's sovereignty.

REVIEW IT!
The theme of Daniel is the sovereignty of God over world history.

MEMORY VERSE

Let the name of God be blessed forever and ever,
For wisdom and power belong to Him.

DANIEL 2:20

DANIEL
[God's Supremacy over Nations]

DAY TWO

COMPLETE READ: Chapters 4–6
QUICK READ: Chapter 4

PROMINENT PLAYER NUMBER 1

> The king's heart is like channels of water in the hand
>   of the LORD;
> He turns it wherever He wishes. (Proverbs 21:1)

> Do you not know? Have you not heard? . . .
> He it is who reduces rulers to nothing,
> Who makes the judges of the earth meaningless.
> Scarcely have they been planted,
> Scarcely have they been sown,
> Scarcely has their stock taken root in the earth,
> But He merely blows on them, and they wither.
>   (Isaiah 40:21,23-24)

The earth has many kings, heaven only One. And that One always carries the day. Regardless of their self-confidence, pride, and power, the earth's kings are no match for heaven's.

On the morning of the battle of Waterloo, Napoleon claimed, "At the end of the day, England will be at the feet of France, and Wellington will be the prisoner of Napoleon." His commanding officer reminded him, "But we must not forget that man proposes and God disposes." With typical arrogance, Napoleon replied, "I want you to understand, sir, that Napoleon proposes and Napoleon disposes." That day God sent rain and hail, making it impossible for Napoleon's planned maneuvers to be carried out. By night, France was at the feet of England, and

WOW!
The statue in Daniel 3:1 was nine feet wide and ninety feet high!

The proud man hath no God.
—JOSEPH HALL, seventeenth-century bishop, satirist, poet, and preacher

Napoleon was the prisoner of Wellington.[1]

Napoleon's predecessor in pride was King Nebuchadnezzar of Babylonia. At the beginning of Daniel 3, King Nebuchadnezzar was at the height of his power, prestige, and pride. Read 3:1-7 and describe what took place.

INTERESTING! Nebuchadnezzar may have been afflicted with an ailment called lycanthropy— a psychosis in which a person imagines himself to be an animal.

Use as many words and phrases as you can to describe Nebuchadnezzar's attitude.

Chapter 4, your Quick Read for today, describes God's dealings with Nebuchadnezzar. Keep in mind the two biblical passages at the beginning of this study as you work through the following questions.

Describe in your own words the dream Nebuchadnezzar told of in 4:1-18.

When a man is wrapped up in himself he makes a pretty small package.
—JOHN RUSKIN, English critic, essayist, and reformer

Summarize Daniel's interpretation of Nebuchadnezzar's visions, found in verses 19-26.

Compare Daniel's advice to him in verse 27 with Nebuchadnezzar's attitude twelve months later in verse 30. How might the difference be explained?

Read verses 31-33. How were Proverbs 21:1 and Isaiah 40:21,23-24, the Scripture passages at the beginning of this lesson, demonstrated in Nebuchadnezzar's life?

After some time, God restored the king to his previous station. Verses 34-37 describe Nebuchadnezzar's response. Summarize what he said and give your opinion of his sincerity.

This scene is an obvious and somewhat unique display of God's sovereign control. What new thoughts have you had about man's power and God's sovereignty?

MEMORY VERSE

Let the name of God be blessed forever and ever,
For wisdom and power belong to Him.

DANIEL 2:20

DANIEL
[God's Supremacy over Nations]

DID YOU KNOW?
Daniel lived just a few
years before Confucius.

DAY THREE

COMPLETE READ: Chapters 7–8
QUICK READ: Chapter 6

PROMINENT PLAYER NUMBER 2

A person of integrity is someone who acts the same whether they are being watched or not.

In his book *Defining Moments*, Rick Ezell says that integrity is to personal character as "health is to the body or 20/20 vision is to the eyes." He goes on to say,

Integrity is the noblest possession.
—Latin proverb

> Integrity reaches into every room of our lives. It is more far-reaching than our talent, our education, our background or our network of friends. Integrity is a lot like water; it seeps into and out of all the cracks of our lives. And when integrity is lost . . . well, hear the words of an anonymous author who penned, "When wealth is lost, nothing is lost; when health is lost, something is lost; when character is lost, all is lost."[2]

Daniel is our second Prominent Player because he so faithfully embodied integrity. The story of Daniel in the lions' den is the most famous moment of Daniel's integrity, but there are so many more—too many to study in this lesson.

Researchers and writers Jim Kouzes and Barry Posner surveyed nearly 1,500 managers around the nation, asking the question, "What values, personal traits, or characteristics do you look for and admire in your superiors?" The 225 values, traits, and characteristics mentioned were then reduced to 15 categories. The most frequent response? Integrity. Managers wanted to work for someone who "is truthful, is trustworthy, has character, has convictions."[3]

To his friends, to his enemies, to kings, to himself, and to his God, Daniel was a man of integrity.

Read chapter 1 of Daniel and respond to the following questions, keeping in mind that Daniel was only sixteen at the time.

Describe the situation Daniel faced.

Describe the issue of integrity at stake.

Describe Daniel's response to the issue.

Describe the results.

Read chapter 6 of Daniel and respond to the following questions, keeping in mind that Daniel was eighty-three at the time.

Describe the situation Daniel faced.

Never esteem anything as of advantage to thee that shall make thee break thy word or lose thy self-respect.

—MARCUS AURELIUS ANTONINUS, Roman philosopher and emperor

Describe the issue of integrity at stake.

Describe Daniel's response to the issue.

There is no such thing as a minor lapse of integrity.
—Tom Peters, business guru

Describe the results.

Notice that living with integrity does not necessarily bring immediate "good" results. Being cast into the lions' den was a precarious situation! What would you think about Daniel's decision if he had not survived the night?

When you think of this kind of integrity, which person in your life comes to mind? Take a few minutes to write a note to that person, sharing what it means to you that he or she consistently models integrity.

REVIEW IT!
Daniel is a Prominent Player because he consistently modeled integrity.

Memory Verse

Let the name of God be blessed forever and ever,
For wisdom and power belong to Him.

Daniel 2:20

DANIEL
[God's Supremacy over Nations]

DAY FOUR

COMPLETE READ: Chapters 9–10
QUICK READ: Chapter 3

A NOTABLE FEATURE

One of the great church fathers, John Chrysostom, was brought before the emperor, who threatened to banish him if he did not deny Christ. Chrysostom answered,

"You cannot, for the whole world is my Father's land. You can't banish me."

"Then I will take away all your property," said the emperor.

"You cannot. My treasures are in heaven."

"Then I'll take you to a place where there is not a friend to speak to," said the emperor.

"You cannot. I have a friend who is closer than a brother. I shall have Jesus Christ, forever."

"Then I'll take away your life!" threatened the emperor.

Chrysostom answered, "You cannot. My life is hid with God in Christ."

Finally, the emperor said, "What do you do with a man like that?"[4]

Taking a stand for what is right can be one of the most defining moments in any life. Choosing to do so can bring death—the Christian martyrs stand in holy witness to that. But not all stands end so dramatically. Regardless, the impact of such a choice can have lifelong effects.

Never, for sake of peace and quiet, deny your own experience or convictions.

—DAG HAMMARSKJOLD, Christian diplomat and peacemaker

Daniel's three friends faced a life-and-death situation in which they had a choice: stand for their faith in God or give in.

As you read chapter 3, respond to the following questions.

Describe the situation as recorded in 3:1-7.

Daniel's friends were accused and confronted in verses 8-15. What temptations do you think they may have faced at that moment? Explain.

Jesus promised his disciples three things— that they would be completely fearless, absurdly happy and in constant trouble.

—G. K. CHESTERTON, English author

Write down words and phrases to describe their reply to the king in verses 16-18.

Summarize what happened in verses 19-30.

The stand taken by these three men was much like that of three other men many centuries later. Bishops Ridley, Latimer, and Cranmer, leaders of the sixteenth-century Reformation in England, were condemned as heretics during the reign of Queen Mary (1553–1558). Each man was given a chance to recant, and each refused. Cranmer was forced to watch as Ridley and Latimer were taken to a stake outside the city wall. Just before his death, Latimer uttered words that have echoed across the years: "Be of good comfort, Master Ridley, and play the man! We shall this day light such a candle, by God's grace, in England, as I trust shall never be put out."[5]

Most of us will never be asked to take that kind of stand. But as we follow Christ and seek to live godly lives, we each will face our own "moments of truth." What have those moments looked like in your life thus far?

What internal struggles do you face when taking those stands?

Talk to God about what is on your mind right now.

MEMORY VERSE

Let the name of God be blessed forever and ever,
For wisdom and power belong to Him.

DANIEL 2:20

DANIEL
[God's Supremacy over Nations]

AMAZING!
Nothing negative is
written about Daniel.

DAY FIVE

COMPLETE READ: Chapters 11–12
QUICK READ: Chapter 9

A TIMELESS PRINCIPLE

> If . . . My people who are called by My name humble themselves and pray and seek My face and turn from their wicked ways, then I will hear from heaven, will forgive their sin and will heal their land. (2 Chronicles 7:13-14)

This promise was given by God, through Solomon, to the people at the dedication of the temple in 959 BC. In 538 BC, 421 years later, Daniel, still an exile in Babylonia at age eighty-three, took God up on His promise. Daniel 9 records his prayer for deliverance, which is our Timeless Principle.

The scene is this: The Jews had been in exile in Babylonia for sixty-seven years. And Daniel had been there the entire time. In the first year of King Darius's reign, Daniel was reading the Word of God and learned that God had promised deliverance for His people after a period of seventy years (Daniel 9:1-2).

Read Jeremiah 25:8-13 and 29:10-14—the very words Daniel read in 538 BC. His prayer in Daniel 9:4-19 resulted after he read this section of Scripture. Daniel's prayer includes elements of confession, adoration, and petition. Meditate on these verses and respond to the following questions.

I fear John Knox's prayers more than an army of ten thousand men.

—MARY, QUEEN OF SCOTS, Roman Catholic leader of the Counter Reformation in Scotland, speaking of the leader of the Protestant Reformation there

What words and phrases did Daniel use to describe the people's sins?

DID YOU KNOW?
The ashes of Daniel 9:3 were the traditional symbol of grief and humility.

What results of their sins as a nation did he acknowledge?

In what ways did Daniel praise and adore God for who He is and what He had done?

Every great movement of God can be traced to a kneeling figure.
—DWIGHT L. MOODY, American evangelist

Verses 16-19 record Daniel's actual petition. Write down your thoughts about the following:

The location of the petition within the rest of the prayer

The attitude of Daniel as he petitioned God

The content of the actual petition

In this case, verses 20-27 show that Daniel's prayer was answered immediately and in great detail. Even though this does not always happen, what can you learn from these verses about God's response to prayer?

Record one or two new thoughts you have had about your prayer life while studying Daniel's prayer. How can they strengthen your relationship with your heavenly Father?

I have had prayers answered—most strangely so sometimes—but I think our heavenly Father's lovingkindness has been even more evident in what He has refused me.

—Lewis Carroll, English author of *Alice in Wonderland*

Memory Verse

Let the name of God be blessed forever and ever, For wisdom and power belong to Him.

Daniel 2:20

DANIEL
[God's Supremacy over Nations]

REVIEW

1. The theme of Daniel is the _____ of God over world history.

2. _____ is a Prominent Player in showing God's sovereignty over the kings of the earth.

3. Daniel is a Prominent Player because he consistently modeled _____ .

4. A Notable Feature of the book is the description of Daniel's three friends taking a stand for their _____ .

5. "Let the _____ of God be blessed forever and ever, For wisdom and power belong to Him."

DANIEL 2:_____

Comprehensive Review of
THE MAJOR PROPHETS

Isaiah

1. The theme of Isaiah is that _____ is of God.

2. Chapter 1 is our Crucial Chapter because it pictures the fourfold theme of the prophets and shows the domino effect of _____ .

3. Isaiah is our Prominent Player whose call by God can teach us much about our
_____ .

4. Chapter 53 is our Notable Feature because of its description of the future _____ of Jesus for our salvation.

5. "'Come now, and let us reason together,'
   Says the LORD,
   'Though your _____ are as scarlet,
   They will be white as snow;
   Though they are red like crimson,
   They will be like wool.'"

ISAIAH 1:_____

Jeremiah

1. The theme of Jeremiah is judgment, judgment, _____ .

2. Chapter 2 is our Crucial Chapter because it illustrates Jeremiah's messages and the road to _____ .

3. Jeremiah is our Prominent Player because he modeled how to endure trials with
_____ .

4. A Notable Feature of the book of Jeremiah is the metaphor of the _____ because it gives insight into the sovereignty of God.

5. "'For my people have _____ Me,
   They burn incense to worthless gods
   And they have stumbled from their ways,
   From the ancient paths,
   To walk in bypaths,
   Not on a highway.'"

JEREMIAH 18:_____

LAMENTATIONS

1. The theme of Lamentations is mourning the fall of _____ .

2. Chapter 1 is our Crucial Chapter because it so graphically illustrates the utter _____ of the city and the sorrow of its people.

3. The Prominent Player in this lament is _____ , in who He is and what He does.

4. Our Notable Feature is Jeremiah's _____ expression of disappointment, confusion, and even anger directed at God.

5. "The LORD's _____ indeed never cease,
   For His compassions never fail.
   They are new every morning;
   Great is Your faithfulness."

LAMENTATIONS 3:_____-_____

Ezekiel

1. The theme of Ezekiel is the glory of God through judgment and _____ .

2. Chapter 1 is a Crucial Chapter because it introduces the theme of the _____ of God.

3. Ezekiel is our Prominent Player because his _____ is the carrying out of a call by God.

4. A Notable Feature in Ezekiel is his _____ of the message.

5. "Then the _____ lifted me up, and I heard a great rumbling sound behind me, 'Blessed be the glory of the LORD in His place.'"

EZEKIEL 3:_____

Daniel

1. The theme of Daniel is the _____ of God over world history.

2. _____ is a Prominent Player in showing God's sovereignty over the kings of the earth.

3. Daniel is a Prominent Player because he consistently modeled _____ .

4. A Notable Feature of the book is the description of Daniel's three friends taking a stand for their _____ .

5. "Let the _____ of God be blessed forever and ever, For wisdom and power belong to Him."

DANIEL 2:_____

CONGRATULATIONS!

You have now completed the fifth set of *The Amazing Collection: The Bible, Book by Book*! You have seen God the Creator in The Pentateuch, God the King in The Kingdom Books, God the Restorer in The Post-Exilic Books, the Sovereign God of wisdom and beauty in The Poetical Books, and the God of Judgment in The Major Prophets. And you have listened to real-life testimonies of women today who have had dynamic encounters with this same God of the Bible. He who was still is!

The sixth set will focus on The Early Minor Prophets. Like the authors of The Major Prophets, these men were chosen by God to deliver messages of future judgment and hope. They were ordinary men who were given an extraordinary task. These books are called "minor" because they are shorter than the major prophetical books, but their messages are just as powerful. Those that were written earlier are called The Early Minor Prophets. They were written approximately 850–700 BC. The Later Minor Prophets were written approximately 665–425 BC.

These next six books are filled with beautiful images of God's great love, His unfailing mercy, and His earnest call to His people to obey. Over and over you will see that God means exactly what He says and that though He is a God of unfailing love, He is also a God who demands obedience and loyalty.

Through vivid word pictures, He clearly spells out what is expected of man and what man can expect from God. As we continue this great journey through God's Word, we hope you are learning for life about every book of the Bible. We also pray you are learning for life about the God of the Bible who has called you into a love relationship with Himself.

We have traveled far, but there is still much ahead of us. So let the adventure continue!

Chronological Relationship of the Old Testament Books

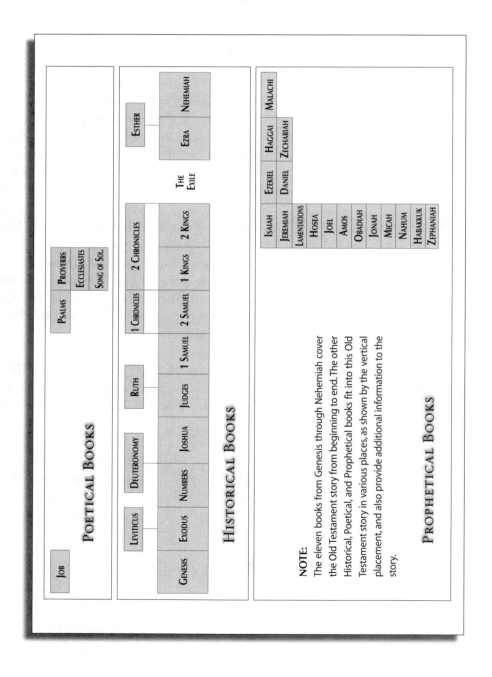

POETICAL BOOKS

Job

Psalms — Proverbs, Ecclesiastes, Song of Sol.

HISTORICAL BOOKS

Genesis, Exodus, Leviticus, Numbers, Deuteronomy, Joshua, Judges, Ruth, 1 Samuel, 2 Samuel, 1 Chronicles, 1 Kings, 2 Chronicles, 2 Kings, The Exile, Esther, Ezra, Nehemiah

NOTE:

The eleven books from Genesis through Nehemiah cover the Old Testament story from beginning to end. The other Historical, Poetical, and Prophetical books fit into this Old Testament story in various places, as shown by the vertical placement, and also provide additional information to the story.

PROPHETICAL BOOKS

Isaiah, Jeremiah, Lamentations, Ezekiel, Daniel, Haggai, Zechariah, Malachi, Hosea, Joel, Amos, Obadiah, Jonah, Micah, Nahum, Habakkuk, Zephaniah

ANSWER KEY TO OUTLINES

ISAIAH

I. **ISAIAH'S PROPHECY OF JUDGMENT—NEED FOR SALVATION (ISAIAH 1–35)**

A. JUDAH had rebelled and would be judged by being exiled.

B. Isaiah saw God as JUDGE and KING—high, lifted up, exalted, and holy.

C. When Isaiah was in God's presence he:

1. Was CONVICTED of his sin.

2. CONFESSED his sin.

3. Was CLEANSED of his sin.

4. Was CALLED to go for the Lord.

D. ISRAEL had rebelled and would be judged by Assyria.

E. Ten NATIONS had rebelled and would be judged.

F. The entire EARTH had rebelled and would be judged "in that day."

II. **HISTORICAL TRANSITION—FROM ASSYRIA TO BABYLON (ISAIAH 36–39)**

A. The ASSYRIANS were threatening to invade Judah.

B. Hezekiah became mortally ILL.

C. Hezekiah was proud. He showed the king of BABYLON all the riches of Judah.

III. **ISAIAH'S PROPHECY OF HOPE—PROVISION OF SALVATION (ISAIAH 40–66)**

A. Isaiah prophesied a <u>VOICE</u> calling, "clear the way for the Lord."

B. Isaiah prophesied <u>CYRUS</u> would rebuild Jerusalem and the temple.

C. Isaiah prophesied a <u>SAVIOR</u> would come. The Savior would:

1. <u>COMFORT</u> His people.

2. <u>SUFFER</u> for sinners.

3. <u>INVITE</u> everybody to come to Him.

4. Heal the brokenhearted and <u>FREE</u> the prisoner.

D. Isaiah prophesied the Savior also would (at His second coming):

1. <u>JUDGE</u> with vengeance.

2. <u>RESTORE</u> Israel.

3. <u>CREATE</u> a new heaven and a new earth.

4. <u>REIGN</u> as King of kings.

JEREMIAH

I. **THE TIMES OF JEREMIAH**

A. King <u>JOSIAH</u> reigned thirty-one years and brought about a spiritual revival.

1. He rid Judah of all the <u>IDOLS</u>.

2. Josiah <u>DIED</u> in a battle with Egypt.

B. The people chose <u>JEHOAHAZ</u>, Josiah's middle son, to serve as king.

1. He served for <u>THREE</u> months.

2. He was exiled to <u>EGYPT</u> and died there.

C. Egypt put <u>JEHOIKIM</u>, Josiah's firstborn, on the throne.

1. He was an <u>EVIL</u> king.

2. He served <u>ELEVEN</u> years.

3. He taxed the people heavily and forced them to build his PALACE.

4. Jeremiah pronounced a CURSE on him.

5. Jehoikim died of NATURAL causes.

D. JEHOICHIN, Jehoikim's son, became king.

1. He reigned three MONTHS.

2. He was exiled to BABYLON.

E. Babylon put ZEDEKIAH on the throne, and he reigned eleven years.

1. Babylon laid a SIEGE around Jerusalem for eighteen months.

2. In July 586 BC, Jerusalem and the TEMPLE were utterly destroyed.

II. THE MAN JEREMIAH

A. God CONSECRATED Jeremiah before he was born.

B. Jeremiah was commanded not to MARRY, have children, or attend funerals or celebrations.

C. Jeremiah endured incredible PERSECUTION.

D. He was a man of incredible COURAGE and tender emotions.

E. He was spared by Nebuchadnezzar and offered ANYTHING he wanted.

F. He chose to stay in JERUSALEM.

G. He wrote a letter to the exiles in BABYLON and encouraged them to settle down there.

H. He gave hope and encouragement by predicting the exiles would return after SEVENTY years.

III. THE MINISTRY AND MESSAGE OF JEREMIAH

A. Josiah's reign: Jeremiah condemned Judah for false worship and promised JUDGMENT.

B. Jehoiakim's reign: Jeremiah promised JUDGMENT for the continuous rebellion against God.

C. Zedekiah's reign: He urged Judah to SURRENDER to Babylon and be saved or face God's judgment.

D. Gedaliah's rule: Jeremiah MINISTERED to those left in Jerusalem.

E. Jeremiah predicted the coming MESSIAH and the Millennial Kingdom.

F. He prophesied judgment on TEN nations.

LAMENTATIONS

I. JEREMIAH DESCRIBED JERUSALEM'S DESOLATION (LAMENTATIONS 1).

A. The city was DESERTED by its inhabitants and former friends.

B. The city was DEVASTATED; nothing was as it was. There was no comfort.

II. JEREMIAH DESCRIBED JERUSALEM'S DESTRUCTION (LAMENTATIONS 2).

A. In anger, the Lord DESTROYED the city as a judgment.

1. God's hand of protection was removed.

2. God abandoned His temple.

3. God silenced the prophets and elders.

B. Jeremiah delivered a message of BLAME to Jerusalem's unfaithful.

III. JEREMIAH DESCRIBED HIS DESPAIR (LAMENTATIONS 3).

A. Jeremiah voiced feelings of personal DEPRESSION at what he saw.

B. Jeremiah expressed faith by declaring there was HOPE for God's chosen.

IV. JEREMIAH DESCRIBED JERUSALEM'S DEFEAT (LAMENTATIONS 4).

A. Jeremiah witnessed the SIEGE of the city and relayed the conditions.

B. Jeremiah listed the REASONS for Jerusalem's defeat.

C. Jeremiah prophesied the enemy's future END.

V. JEREMIAH DESCRIBED JERUSALEM'S DESPONDENCY (LAMENTATIONS 5).

   A. Jeremiah <u>CONFESSED</u> and <u>INTERCEDED</u> for the people in prayer.

   B. Jeremiah <u>PLEADED</u> with God to intervene for His children.

EZEKIEL

I. THE HISTORY OF JUDAH

   A. Judah was <u>EXILED</u> three times in twenty years by Babylon.

      1. The <u>FIRST</u> exile in 605 BC, Babylon deported Daniel.

      2. The <u>SECOND</u> exile in 597 BC, Babylon deported King Jehoiakim and ten thousand others.

      3. The <u>THIRD</u> and final exile in 586 BC, Babylon deported the rest of the educated people and completely destroyed the temple and the city of Jerusalem.

   B. The book of Ezekiel took place and was written before, during, and after the third and final exile.

      1. <u>BABYLON</u> was the supreme world power at that time.

      2. <u>NEBUCHADNEZZAR</u> was the ruler of Babylon.

      3. The young, godly prophet <u>DANIEL</u> was already in a position of power and influence in the Babylonian court.

II. THE HISTORY OF EZEKIEL (EZEKIEL 1–3)

   A. Ezekiel spent his youth in <u>JUDAH</u>.

      1. Ezekiel was trained as a <u>PRIEST</u>.

      2. Ezekiel was probably a pupil of the godly prophet <u>JEREMIAH</u>.

      3. Ezekiel was about seventeen during the <u>FIRST</u> exile.

   B. Ezekiel was deported during the <u>SECOND</u> exile around the age of twenty-five.

      1. Ezekiel lived in an area near Tel-Abib, a <u>JEWISH</u> colony.

2. Ezekiel ministered to the <u>EXILES</u> in captivity for twenty-two years.

3. Ezekiel prophesied through <u>SIGNS</u> (also: symbols, poetry, proverbs, and parables).

III. THE JUDGMENT ON JUDAH (EZEKIEL 4–24)

A. Ezekiel prophesied about the third exile and the destruction of the <u>TEMPLE</u> and the city.

B. Ezekiel preached that God's <u>GLORY</u> would depart from the temple and the area of Judah.

C. Ezekiel warned the people to <u>RETURN</u> to God if they wanted to <u>RETURN</u> to Jerusalem.

IV. THE JUDGMENT ON OTHER NATIONS (EZEKIEL 25–32)

A. Ezekiel prophesied judgment against Israel's cruel <u>NEIGHBORS</u>.

B. Ezekiel prophesied judgment against the great <u>NATIONS</u> of the day.

V. THE RESTORATION OF JUDAH (EZEKIEL 33–48)

A. Ezekiel assured the people that God's <u>RESTORATION</u> was sure.

B. Ezekiel told the people that God would give them a <u>NEW</u> heart, spirit, and beginning.

C. Ezekiel gave the people specific instructions on <u>REBUILDING</u> the temple and the city.

DANIEL

I. PERSONAL HISTORY OF DANIEL (DANIEL 1–6)

A. Daniel and his friends refused Babylon's food to keep God's dietary laws.

1. Result: God gave them health, wisdom, and <u>UNDERSTANDING</u>.

2. Lesson: Trusting the Sovereign God brings God's <u>POWER</u>.

B. Daniel interpreted Nebuchadnezzar's first dream:

    1. Dream: A <u>STATUE</u> with gold head, silver chest, bronze thighs, iron legs, iron/clay feet

    2. Interpretation: There would be four future Gentile <u>KINGDOMS</u>.

C. Daniel's three friends refused to worship Nebuchadnezzar's image.

    1. Result: All three were thrown into the fiery <u>FURNACE</u>.

    2. Lesson: Trusting the Sovereign God brings God's <u>PRESENCE</u>.

D. Daniel interpreted Nebuchadnezzar's second dream:

    1. Dream: A <u>TREE</u> chopped down leaving a stump

    2. Interpretation: Nebuchadnezzar was the tree. He would be cut down by insanity until he repented of <u>PRIDE</u>.

E. Daniel interpreted God's message at King Belshazzar's feast:

    1. Message: A hand <u>WRITING</u> on the wall

    2. Interpretation: Belshazzar's kingdom would <u>END</u>. That very night Belshazzar died.

F. Daniel refused King Darius's order not to petition any god but him.

    1. Result: Daniel was thrown into the <u>LIONS</u>' den.

    2. Lesson: Trusting the Sovereign God brings God's <u>PROTECTION</u>.

II. UNIVERSAL PROPHECIES OF DANIEL (DANIEL 7–12)

A. Vision of Four Great Beasts

    1. The beasts are the four future <u>GENTILE</u> kingdoms.

    2. The fourth kingdom ruler who wages war with the saints is the <u>ANTICHRIST</u>.

B. Vision of a Ram and Goat

    1. The ram with two horns pictures the Medes-<u>PERSIANS</u>.

    2. The goat has one horn and pictures the <u>GREEKS</u>. The goat would defeat the ram (the Greeks defeated the Persians).

3. Chapter 8 is history (second and third kingdoms).

C. Vision of 70 Weeks

    1. To the Jews, a "week" meant <u>7 YEARS</u>. In 70 weeks (70 x 7 years) or 490 years, God would deal with sin of Israel.

    2. From decree to rebuild wall of Jerusalem there would be 7 weeks (7 x 7 years) or 49 years until the wall was complete.

    3. After an additional 62 weeks (7 weeks + 62 weeks = 69 weeks x 7 years) or 483 years, <u>MESSIAH</u> would come.

    4. There is one prophetic week (7 years) left!

D. Vision of the Last "Week" and "Prince to Come"

    1. The "prince to come" (Antichrist) would make a covenant for 1 week (7 years) but after 3 ½ years would bring in abominations.

    2. There would be a time of <u>DISTRESS</u> unlike the nation of Israel had ever known.

    3. The outcome: People will make a decision—for God or against God.

NOTES

ISAIAH

1. J. Sidlow Baxter, *Explore the Book*, vol. 3 (Grand Rapids, Mich.: Zondervan, 1960), p. 217.

2. John Bright, *A History of Israel* (Philadelphia: Westminster, 1959), p. 288.

3. Os Guinness, *The Call* (Nashville: Word, 1998), pp. 8-9.

4. Søren Kierkegaard, quoted in Guinness, p. 3.

5. "O Sacred Head, Now Wounded," *Hymns for the Family of God* (Nashville: Paragon Associates, Inc., 1976), p. 284.

6. Kenneth W. Osbeck, *101 More Hymn Stories* (Grand Rapids, Mich.: Kregel, 1985), p. 218.

7. "O Sacred Head, Now Wounded," p. 284.

8. Paul Lee Tan, *Encyclopedia of 7700 Illustrations: Signs of the Times* (Rockville, Md.: Assurance Publishers, 1979), p. 1383.

JEREMIAH

1. *Webster's New Collegiate Dictionary* (Springfield, Mass.: G&C Merriam Co. Publishers, 1960), p. 408.

2. Roy B. Zuck, "Hanging Tough in Tough Times," *Connection: Extra Topics of Interest to DTS Alumni*.

3. Theo. Laetsch, *Jeremiah* (Saint Louis, Mo.: Concordia, 1965), pp. xi-xii.

4. G. Christian Weiss, *Insights into Bible Times and Customs* (Chicago: Moody, 1972), p. 45.

5. Weiss, p. 46.

LAMENTATIONS

1. Thomas O. Chisholm, "Great Is Thy Faithfulness," *Hymns for the Family of God* (Nashville: Paragon Associates, Inc., 1976), p. 98.

2. Philip Yancey, *The Bible Jesus Read* (Grand Rapids, Mich.: Zondervan, 1999), pp. 128-129.

3. Kenneth W. Osbeck, *101 Hymn Stories* (Grand Rapids, Mich.: Kregel, 1982), p. 84.

4. Chisholm, p. 98.

EZEKIEL

1. Søren Kierkegaard, quoted in Os Guinness, *The Call* (Nashville: Word, 1998), p. 3.

2. Guinness, p. 4.

3. John Piper, *The Supremacy of God in Preaching* (Grand Rapids, Mich.: Baker, 1990), p. 10.

4. Piper, p. 9.

DANIEL

1. David Jeremiah, *The Handwriting on the Wall* (Dallas: Word, 1992), pp. 86-87.

2. Rick Ezell, *Defining Moments* (Downers Grove, Ill.: InterVarsity, 2001), p. 72.

3. James M. Kouzes and Barry Z. Posner, *The Leadership Challenge* (San Francisco: Jossey-Bass, 1987), p. 16.

4. Jeremiah, p. 84.

5. James Emery White, *Life-Defining Moments* (Colorado Springs, Colo.: WaterBrook, 2001), p. 84.

LEADER'S GUIDE

1. *Webster's New Collegiate Dictionary* (Springfield, Mass.: G&C Merriam Co. Publishers, 1960), p. 237.

2. John K. Brilhart, *Effective Group Discussion* (Dubuque, Iowa: Wm. C. Brown Company Publishers, 1967), p. 26.

3. *How to Lead Small Group Bible Studies* (Colorado Springs, Colo.: NavPress, 1982), pp. 40-42.

BIOGRAPHIES

PAT HARLEY
Teacher

Pat committed her life to Jesus Christ at the age of thirty-two after He powerfully intervened and healed her broken marriage. After eight years of study, she began teaching the Bible to women, convinced that it is the Word of God that offers help and hope for women today. She is the founder and president of Big Dream Ministries, Inc. and served for eighteen years as the director of The Women's Fellowship, a former ministry to over five hundred women. She also served as the director of women's ministries at Fellowship Bible Church in Roswell, Georgia. Pat has a master of arts degree in education from Western Michigan University and is currently working on a degree from Dallas Theological Seminary. She and her husband have two married daughters and several grandchildren.

ELEANOR LEWIS
Teacher

At the age of twenty-six, Eleanor accepted Christ for assurance of heaven. However, when her son was born with a severe birth defect, she turned to God's Word for answers and found not only a Savior but an all-powerful Lord. The Word of God came alive for her, and she began teaching and speaking at Christian women's clubs. For almost thirty years, she has taught Bible studies in churches, homes, and offices. In addition, she speaks at conferences and retreats across the country and internationally. She is president of Insights and Beginnings, Inc., which produced a video series and Bible study to help people understand their temperament types, overcome weaknesses, and use their strengths for the glory of God. Eleanor and her husband live in the Atlanta area and have a married son and one grandchild.

MARGIE RUETHER
Teacher

Though Margie was not raised in a churchgoing home, her parents committed their lives to Christ after Margie was in college. It was her mother's godly example and prayers that brought Margie to the throne of grace. Her growing love for Jesus and His Word led her to Bible Study Fellowship International, an interdenominational Christian organization in which laypeople teach Bible studies. After many years of study, she became a substitute teaching leader and a member of the area team. She served there for a number of years before becoming one of the lead teachers at The Women's Fellowship in Roswell, Georgia. She has also facilitated a Bible teacher-training program for women and speaks at retreats and church conferences. She and her two children live in the Atlanta area.

LINDA SWEENEY
Teacher

Linda accepted Christ as her personal Savior when she was twelve years old. As an adult, she grew to love God's Word more and more. Because of her passion to excite women to know the Word and to see their lives change as they respond in obedience, she began teaching the Bible to women in her community. She has taught Sunday school classes for more than twenty-five years and was a much-loved Bible Study Fellowship teaching leader for eight years. During that time, she not only taught hundreds of women weekly but also trained as many as seventy-five Bible Study Fellowship leaders. She has taught women's retreats throughout the South. She and her husband live in the Atlanta area and have a married daughter, a son, and two grandchildren.

ART VANDER VEEN
Senior Copywriter

Art began his relationship with Christ at age thirteen. In his late twenties after graduating from the University of New Mexico, he began preparing for full-time ministry. He earned a Th.M. degree from Dallas Theological Seminary and has ministered on the staff of Campus Crusade for Christ. He was one of the original team members of Walk Thru the Bible Ministries and served as chaplain for the Atlanta Falcons. In 1979, he was part of a team that founded Fellowship Bible Church in Roswell, Georgia, where he was a pastor for nearly twenty-five years. He now serves as pastor, teacher, and mentor at Little Branch Community Church in the Atlanta area. Art is passionate about helping people understand the Scriptures as the revealed truth from and about God. He and his wife, Jan, have three married children and seven grandchildren.

CARRIE OTT
Editor, Designer

Carrie met Christ at an early age. All her life she has had a passion for words, and as a freelance writer and designer, this passion doubles when it is words — seen, read, and grasped — that attempt to sketch a portrait of the mystery and wonder of God and His Word. Carrie identifies with Mechtild of Magdeburg, who said, "Of the heavenly things God has shown me, I can speak but a little word, no more than a honeybee can carry away on its foot from an overflowing jar." Carrie and her husband have three children and live in the Atlanta area.

To learn more about
Big Dream Ministries, Inc. and
The Amazing Collection,
visit their website at:

www.theamazingcollection.org

LEADER'S GUIDE

INTRODUCTION

Leading a group Bible study can be a challenging but incredibly rewarding experience. This Leader's Guide will provide help with the "challenging" part, as you trust God to produce the "incredibly rewarding" piece.

This guide is not designed to take you step-by-step through the individual studies. Instead, it will offer some general guidance and instruction in principles and techniques. Most of what you learn here will not be specific to *The Amazing Collection* but applicable to many kinds of group study. The one exception is Appendix B.

Each section of this Leader's Guide will deal with a single subject, making it easier for you to return to the guide for future help and reference.

Thank you for accepting the challenge and responsibility of leading your group! We pray God will make this a rewarding and profitable experience for you.

DISCUSSION: THE ESSENTIAL COMPONENT

The words *small-group Bible study* are almost synonymous with the term *discussion*. While there are very significant places and purposes for lecturing (one-way communication), for the most part a small group is not one of them. Therefore, discussion is an essential component of a successful small-group experience.

Discussion is the investigation of a subject or question by two or more people using verbal dialogue. Webster defines it as "consideration of a question in open debate; argument for the sake of arriving at truth or clearing up difficulties." Additionally, the word *discuss* and its synonyms mean "to discourse about so as to reach conclusions or to convince. Discuss also implies a sifting or examining, especially by presenting considerations pro and con."[1]

Small-group Bible studies will not always include debate or argument, but there *should* always be investigation, examination, and the reaching of at least tentative conclusions.

There are many benefits to discussion-style learning compared to lectures or even to interaction that is dominated by one person. Discussion:

- Keeps every member more involved in the learning process
- Allows for self-disclosure, enabling the participants to get to know each other better
- Helps crystallize the thinking of each group member by creating a venue in which topics can be investigated at deeper levels
- Creates a more informal atmosphere, which encourages a sense of relaxed learning
- Provides the potential of uncovering misconceptions and correcting misinformation
- Fosters more permanent learning and change because people tend to better remember what is said rather than what is thought
- Builds a sense of community as participants cooperate in their search for truth and understanding

While small-group Bible studies that foster healthy discussion will realize the above benefits, the depth of any group experience is greatly enhanced by an able leader. The leader plays an important role in helping each of these seven benefits become reality. For example, in order to keep every member more involved in the learning process, the leader will need to encourage those who tend to hide and manage those who tend to dominate. The other benefits require similar sensitivity by the leader. The remainder of this guide is intended to help the leader maximize these benefits for her small group.

But before we move on, one more issue should be addressed. While the leader is a crucial player in a small group, she should not become the person to whom all other participants address their remarks. One author has suggested that a discussion leader should strive to foster an "all-channel" network, rather than become the "hub" or center of a discussion wheel, as the following diagrams depict.

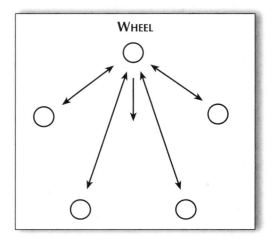

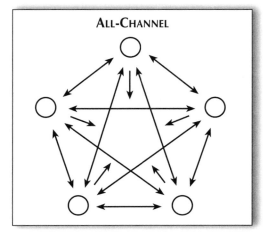

In a "wheel" network, all comments are directed toward one central leader, and he or she alone speaks to the group as a whole or to any one person.

By contrast, an "all-channel" network allows rapid communication without requiring clearance from a central gatekeeper; everyone is free to share thoughts that come to mind while they are still relevant to the topic at hand. Free exchange of questions and responses is thus encouraged.[2]

The leader's responsibility is to continually remind herself of the need for "all-channel" communication.

LISTENING: THE LOST ART

You've probably heard it said that God gave us two ears and one mouth because He wanted us to listen twice as much as we talk. It would be difficult to prove that assumption, but the Bible *does* say:

> But everyone must be quick to hear, slow to speak. (James 1:19)

> He who gives an answer before he hears,
> It is folly and shame to him. (Proverbs 18:13)

Listening may be the most powerful tool of a successful small-group leader, but it is also possibly the most difficult trait to develop. Most people tend to talk more than listen, be more concerned about their interests than the interests of others, and listen impatiently, hoping the other person will finish quickly. True listening is a lost art, which a good small-group leader must recapture.

Listening is not just hearing. As reading is to seeing, listening is to hearing. By both reading and listening, we understand the real meaning of the words our senses "take in."

Consider the following ideas and use them to evaluate your own listening habits and skills. Then, decide which areas you could intentionally improve.

Listening Characteristics:

- It is active, not passive, and therefore sometimes tiring.

- It is other-centered, not self-centered, and therefore sometimes sacrificial.

- It is crucial, not peripheral, and therefore indispensable.

- It is difficult, not easy, and therefore often neglected.

- It is scarce, not common, and therefore greatly desirable.

Listening is not like:

- A chess game — planning your next verbal move while the other person is talking
- A trial — judging what is said or how it is said
- A 100-yard dash — thinking how quickly you can end the discussion

Listening is like:

- A sponge — absorbing as much as possible of what is being said and the feelings behind it
- A pair of binoculars — fixing attention on and bringing into clear focus what is being said

Kinds of Questions:

- Information — "What did you do today?"
- Opinion — "Why do you think that happened?"
- Feeling — "How do you feel about that?"

Kinds of Responses:

- Clarification — "I think what you're saying is . . ." This gets at the meaning of what was said.
- Observation — "I noticed that your voice dropped when . . ." This acknowledges the importance of nonverbal cues.
- Reflection — "You seem quite sad about . . ." This acknowledges the emotional component.
- Inquiry — "Tell me more about . . ." This seeks additional information and often gleans further insight.

While you are listening, consider silently praying for wisdom:

- "God, what are you doing in this person's heart right now?"
- "Father, help me to hear what she is really saying."
- "Eternal Counselor, what kind of response do you want me to make to what this person is saying?"

There will be times as a small-group leader when you will need to limit one member's input to allow for total group input. Your aim is not to encourage never-ending dialogue with one person, but to bring the most and the best out of each participant and the group as a whole, maximizing discussion, insight, and impact more fully than you may have thought possible.

Questions: The Mental Crowbars

Good questions can spell the difference between success and failure in a small-group setting. As you lead discussions of *The Amazing Collection*, the Learning for Life discussion questions at the beginning of each study will give you an excellent starting point. But there will be times when you will want to probe differently or more deeply. At such times, forming good questions will be incredibly important.

Some of these questions may be prepared ahead of time. Others will be developed as you go. Remember, every good question shares some common characteristics:

- Brief — short and uncluttered
- Applicable — relevant to the people's needs
- Simple — easily understood
- Interesting — capable of holding attention
- Conforming — based on the material being studied

As a leader you may ask launching, guiding, and application questions. The following material describes these three types of questions, giving examples of each.

Launching Questions:
- Initiate meaningful discussion on a subject
- May be prepared ahead of time
- Will determine to a large extent the direction your discussion will take
- Are general questions intended to stimulate discussion
- Must be based on the participants' previous study to enable quality contributions
   Examples:
   - "What did you discover in this passage about . . . ?"
   - "What impressed you most about how God . . . ?"
   - "What thoughts do you have about Moses after this study?"
   - "Why do you think God included this passage in the Bible?"
   - "How would you describe the holiness of God?"

Guiding Questions:
- Keep the discussion moving, drawing out the most important ideas and refocusing a wandering discussion
- May be prepared ahead of time as you anticipate the subjects that will be raised by the group

- May be crafted as the discussion is in high gear (This takes practice!)
- Take the participants beyond initial observations and more deeply into the meaning of the material

  Examples:
  - "Sally just mentioned the concept of obedience. How does that fit with what this passage seems to say?"
  - "Who else would like to comment on that?"
  - "We've said a lot of things about grace in our discussion. If you had to boil it down to a sentence, what would you say?"
  - "What we're discussing is interesting, but we've wandered from where we want to go. Can someone take us back to where we veered off the trail?"

Application Questions:
- Are supplied for you in *The Amazing Collection* workbooks
- May be developed based on your own knowledge of the group
- May be difficult to formulate but serve as the bridge from Bible study to daily living—from the head to the heart
- Do not always involve something concrete to do or to change
- Could include meditation, reflection, remembering, or simply waiting on God
- May be questions that will encourage the group to share their answers aloud or may suggest a more private response
- May be specific or general
- Must relate to the truth the group has just studied

  Examples:
  - "Write a prayer pouring out your heart to God in response to what He has been teaching you this week."
  - "Do you know someone who models well what we have just studied? How could you affirm that person this week?"
  - "What do you sense God is asking you to do in response to your study?"
  - "What do you see in this character's life that you would like to imitate? What would that look like? What is the first step?"

Crafting and asking questions are skills that can be developed and honed. After each group meeting, it might be useful to evaluate your questions. Did they lead the group where you sensed God wanted to lead? Which "as you go" guiding questions worked well or not so well? How did the group respond to the questions? Was there any confusion? Finally, make a point to review anything you learned about asking questions each week.

ROLES PEOPLE PLAY: THE ULTIMATE CHALLENGE

If being a small-group Bible study leader involved only facilitating discussion, learning to listen well, and forging meaningful questions, the challenge would be large enough. But add to that the fact that every person in your group will have different needs, temperaments and personalities, approaches to Bible study, reasons for being there, and levels of maturity, and the role of leadership becomes exponentially more challenging.

Professor Howard Hendricks of Dallas Theological Seminary describes in *How to Lead Small Group Bible Studies* some of the roles people play in group situations. You may find these helpful in evaluating your own group's dynamic.

Immature roles

The onlooker	Content to be a silent spectator. Only nods, smiles, and frowns. Other than this, he is a passenger instead of a crew member.
The monopolizer	Brother Chatty. Rambles roughshod over the rest of the conversation with his verbal dexterity. Tenaciously clings to his right to say what he thinks — even without thinking.
The belittler	This is Mr. Gloom. He minimizes the contributions of others. Usually has three good reasons why some opinion is wrong.
The wisecrack	Feels called to a ministry of humor. Mr. Cheerio spends his time as the group playboy. Indifferent to the subject at hand, he is always ready with a clever remark.
The hitchhiker	Never had an original thought in his life. Unwilling to commit himself. Sits on the sidelines until others reach a conclusion, then jumps on the bandwagon.
The pleader	Chronically afflicted with obsessions. Always pleading for some cause or action. Feels led to share this burden frequently. One-track mind.
The sulker	Lives with a resentful mood. The group won't always agree entirely with his views, so he sulks.

Mature roles

The proposer	Initiates ideas and action. Keeps things moving.
The encourager	Brings others into the discussion. Encourages others to contribute. Emphasizes the value of their suggestions and comments. Stimulates others to greater activity by approval and recognition.

The clarifier	Has the ability to step in when confusion, chaos, and conflict occur. He defines the problem concisely. Points out the issues clearly.
The analyzer	Examines the issues closely. Weighs suggestions carefully. Never accepts anything without first thinking it through.
The explorer	Always moving into new and different areas. Probes relentlessly. Never satisfied with the obvious or the traditional viewpoints.
The mediator	Promotes harmony between members — especially those who have trouble agreeing. Seeks to find conclusions acceptable to all.
The synthesizer	Able to put the pieces together from different ideas and viewpoints.[3]

No doubt you will see some of these roles typified by members of your small group. How you deal with members who play out the immature roles and how you encourage and utilize those who take on the mature ones will be an ongoing challenge. Ask the Spirit of God to give you sensitivity, creativity, and ability as you lead. Pray for wisdom to become your constant, ready resource.

YOUR LEADERSHIP: A SPIRITUAL ENDEAVOR

Before we move on, it is important to remember that beyond understanding and fostering discussion, learning to listen well, developing your skill in fashioning questions, and learning to lead different kinds of people, it is God who supplies the grace and strength that will carry you through the challenges of leadership.

This Leader's Guide has focused so far on you and your best efforts, but in truth you will accomplish absolutely nothing of eternal value unless the Spirit of God takes your faithful efforts and infuses them with His enabling power and grace.

For this reason, we encourage you to prepare and lead in complete humility, dependence, and trust, remembering these critical precepts:

I can do all things through Him who strengthens me. (Philippians 4:13)

"My grace is sufficient for you, for power is perfected in weakness." (2 Corinthians 12:9)

"I am the vine, you are the branches; he who abides in Me and I in him, he bears much fruit, for apart from Me you can do nothing." (John 15:5)

Finally, be strong in the Lord and in the strength of His might. Put on the full armor of God, so that you will be able to stand firm against the schemes of the devil. (Ephesians 6:10-11)

Our prayer for you is that of Paul's prayers for the Ephesians:

> That the God of our Lord Jesus Christ, the Father of glory, may give to you a spirit of wisdom and of revelation in the knowledge of Him. I pray that the eyes of your heart may be enlightened, so that you will know what is the hope of His calling, what are the riches of the glory of His inheritance in the saints, and what is the surpassing greatness of His power toward us who believe. These are in accordance with the working of the strength of His might. . . . [And] that He would grant you, according to the riches of His glory, to be strengthened with power through His Spirit in the inner man, so that Christ may dwell in your hearts through faith; and that you, being rooted and grounded in love, may be able to comprehend with all the saints what is the breadth and length and height and depth, and to know the love of Christ which surpasses knowledge, that you may be filled up to all the fullness of God. Now to Him who is able to do far more abundantly beyond all that we ask or think, according to the power that works within us, to Him be the glory in the church and in Christ Jesus to all generations forever and ever. Amen. (Ephesians 1:17-19; 3:16-21)

APPENDIX A

THE EFFECTIVE DISCUSSION LEADER: A WORTHY GOAL

This section presents a model for the effective discussion leader (EDL). You may not demonstrate every characteristic listed, nor do you need to. Some of these things you will do very well; others you will do okay; still others may be a weak area for you. That is just fine. Consider this list simply an ideal to aim for. Our hope is that it will motivate you to grow as a small-group leader by revealing your areas of strength and highlighting your areas of weakness for which you may need help. God never said He could use only perfect people in ministry. In fact, your limitations in one or more of these areas may allow for others in the group to come alongside and complement you by contributing their strengths.

You may choose to use this list with a group of leaders to discuss your common ministries and responsibilities and share with each other challenges and successes you've experienced as leaders. Hearing others' thoughts about each of these characteristics might encourage you as you continue to grow.

What key characteristics make an effective discussion leader?

1. EDLs have a good grasp of the material to be discussed.
   - They have studied the material in advance.
   - They have a clear purpose for the meeting.
   - They have an introduction planned.
   - They have questions planned.
   - They have a tentative conclusion in mind.
   - They have examined their own life in relation to the truth of the study.
   - They seek to be diligent workers who accurately handle the word of truth (see 2 Timothy 2:15).

2. EDLs are skilled in organizing group thinking.
   - They know how to use questions.

- They can detect tangents and gently but firmly bring the discussion back on track.

3. EDLs are open-minded.
   - They express judgments in a conditional way.
   - They encourage consideration of all points of view.
   - They encourage open-mindedness on the part of all the members.
   - They are able to handle incorrect answers by inviting further questioning or discussion.

4. EDLs are active participants.
   - They talk frequently yet not excessively.
   - They are not defensive or sensitive to disagreement or criticism.

5. EDLs are facilitators.
   - They do not give dictatorial directions.
   - They encourage participation by all.
   - They encourage interaction among all members.
   - They are able to manage members who tend to dominate discussion.
   - They are able to stimulate and involve shy or reticent members in nonthreatening ways.

6. EDLs speak well.
   - They speak clearly.
   - They speak in a concise, pertinent way.
   - They are not tactless, chattering, offensive speakers.

7. EDLs have respect for and sensitivity to others.
   - They are empathetic.
   - They do not attack others.
   - They do not cause others to "lose face."
   - They are aware of how others are reacting.
   - They are patient.

8. EDLs are self-controlled.
   - They can remain impartial when necessary.

- They can express their feelings in a direct, yet nonaccusatory manner.

9. EDLs can assume different roles.
   - They can give encouragement.
   - They can give direction when necessary.
   - They can insert humor to break the tension when appropriate.
   - They can lead the group in prayer to seek wisdom.
   - They can give personal attention to needy members.

10. EDLs give credit to the group and its members.
    - They praise the group for insights and progress.
    - They stress teamwork.
    - They make all the members feel important.
    - They value others as their equals.
    - They "do nothing from selfishness or empty conceit" but regard others as more important than themselves (Philippians 2:3).

11. EDLs are authentically transparent.
    - They share personal illustrations.
    - They share personal weaknesses, frustrations, pressures, and failures without seeking undue personal attention.
    - They share personal feelings.
    - They share personal requests.
    - They plan ahead so all this can be done with taste and genuineness.

12. EDLs are enthusiastic.
    - They pour themselves into the subject and the discussion of it.
    - They allow the subject to be poured into them by God prior to the discussion.
    - They recognize that genuine enthusiasm is a powerful motivator for others.

13. EDLs are properly critical and evaluative of their leadership.
    - They constantly look for ways to improve.
    - They regularly seek feedback and advice.
    - They consistently evaluate the various aspects of their leadership role.

- They remember that evaluation is not comparing themselves with others but is seeking the Holy Spirit's input on possible improvement.

14. EDLs know that leadership is a spiritual endeavor.

   - They regularly admit to God that apart from Him they can do nothing (see John 15:5).

   - They confidently say "I can do all things" and then humbly add "through Him who strengthens me" (Philippians 4:13).

   - They never forget God's promise that "My grace is sufficient for you" (2 Corinthians 12:9).

APPENDIX B

SUGGESTED FORMATS FOR *THE AMAZING COLLECTION*

The Amazing Collection is intentionally flexible to accommodate a variety of teaching settings and calendars. It is possible to complete the study of all sixty-six books of the Bible in two years by teaching a book a week for thirty-three weeks each year (excluding summers and holidays).

Another option would be to go through the material in three years, teaching a book a week for twenty-two weeks each year, perhaps beginning in September and going through April. Also, for individuals, the program could be completed in approximately fifteen months, studying a book a week for sixty-six consecutive weeks.

There is flexibility in each individual session as well. Sessions might last an hour, in which the group watches the video (forty-five minutes) and allows fifteen minutes for discussion. Or, a 1.5-hour format could include the video, fifteen minutes for refreshments, fifteen for discussion, and fifteen for homework review. If time permits, two-hour sessions could include the video, refreshments, thirty minutes for discussion, and thirty for homework review.

Maybe you'll discover another format that suits your group to a tee. Feel free to use it!

APPENDIX C

SHARING THE GOSPEL

Leaders should be sensitive to the fact that some group members may have an interest in the Bible without having established a personal relationship with its central figure, Jesus Christ.

Sharing the gospel is quite easy for some people and more challenging for others. But if you sense that there are members in your group who would benefit from a clear explanation of salvation, by all means, offer one! There may even be "natural" openings during your course of study (at the end of a book or workbook or during your study of the Gospels or the book of Romans) when the gospel seems to "tell itself." In addition, the vast majority of discussion questions (Old and New Testament) contain a question that points directly to the person of Jesus Christ. These are "teachable moments." Don't miss them.

Several excellent tools exist that can help you walk an unbeliever through the basics of salvation. *The Four Spiritual Laws*, *Steps to Peace with God*, *My Heart — Christ's Home*, and *The Roman Road* are just a few. The leaders in your church may be able to provide you with one or more of them.

Although there are many excellent video testimonies throughout *The Amazing Collection*, it may be appropriate at some point to briefly share your own personal testimony with your group or with one or more of its members. It may help to think of your "story" in four parts: your life before Christ, how you came to know and understand your need for forgiveness and reconciliation with God, what Christ did on your behalf on the cross, and how your life is different today having accepted His atoning sacrifice on your behalf. This is your story! Pray for a sensitive heart, the right timing, and the right words to share it when the Holy Spirit leads you to do so.

It is our prayer that no one would complete *The Amazing Collection* without a personal, saving knowledge of our Savior, the Lord Jesus Christ.